S0-BZJ-541

Instructor's Examples Manual

M. K. McGee
Metropolitan Community College

Elementary Algebra
for College Students

Sixth Edition

Allen R. ANGEL

PEARSON
Prentice Hall

Upper Saddle River, NJ 07458

Editor-in-Chief: Chris Hoag
Senior Acquisitions Editor: Paul Murphy
Editorial Assistant: Kerri-Ann O'Donnell
Assistant Managing Editor: John Matthews
Production Editor: Donna Crilly
Supplement Cover Manager: Paul Gourhan
Supplement Cover Designer: Joanne Alexandris
Manufacturing Buyer: Ilene Kahn

© 2004 by Pearson Education, Inc.
Pearson Education, Inc.
Upper Saddle River, NJ 07458

Pearson Prentice Hall. All rights reserved. Printed in the United States of America. This publication is protected by Copyright and permission should be obtained from the publisher prior to any prohibited reproduction, storage in a retrieval system or transmission in any form or by any means, electronic, mechanical, photocopying, recording, or likewise. For information regarding permission(s), write to: Rights and Permissions Department.

Pearson Prentice Hall is a trademark of Pearson Education, Inc.

Printed in the United States of America

10 9 8 7 6 5 4 3 2 1

ISBN 0-13-141761-4

Pearson Education Ltd., *London*
Pearson Education Australia Pty. Ltd., *Sydney*
Pearson Education Singapore, Pte. Ltd.
Pearson Education North Asia Ltd., *Hong Kong*
Pearson Education Canada, Inc., *Toronto*
Pearson Educación de Mexico, S.A. de C.V.
Pearson Education—Japan, *Tokyo*
Pearson Education Malaysia, Pte. Ltd.
Pearson Education, *Upper Saddle River, New Jersey*

Chapter 1: Real Numbers

Section 1.2

EXAMPLE 1:

1A) The Sunshine Shuttle service takes airline passengers to the city center and back again on a daily basis. The distance from the airport to the city center is 13 miles. The shuttle makes 10 roundtrips daily and carries an average of 15 passengers per trip (each way). The fare each way is $15.50.
a) What are the shuttle's receipts from one day's operation?
b) If the one-way fare is increased by 15%, determine the new fare.

1B) The Eastman Parking Garage charges $1.25 for each hour of parking or part thereof. Ricardo parks his car in the garage from 8:00 A.M. to 5:30 P.M., 6 days a week. **a)** What is his weekly cost for parking? **b)** How much would he save by paying a weekly parking rate of $50?

Solutions:
1A) a) $4,650; **b)** $17.83
1B) a) $71.25; **b)** $21.25

EXAMPLE 2:

1A) Suppose a computer processor can perform about 1.3 billion operations per second. How many operations can it perform in 0.7 seconds?
1B) The populations of the United States is approximately 288 million. Suppose that 3% of the population buy a new car every year. How many persons buy a new car every year?

Solutions:
1A) 91,000,000 operations
1B) 8,640,000 persons

EXAMPLE 3:

3A) Suppose a medical insurance policy requires that one pay the first $150 of medical expenses each calendar year (called a deductible). After the deductible is paid, one must pay 25% of the medical expenses (called co-payment) and the insurance company pays 75%. (There is a maximum co-payment of $1000 that one must pay each year. After that, the insurance company pays 100% of the fee schedule.) Suppose an owner of this insurance policy breaks an arm. This person must visit the emergency room and get X rays. The total bill of $1525 is sent to the insurance company. **a)** How much of the bill is the policy owner responsible for? **b)** How much will the insurance company be responsible for?

3B) Consider the same situation as in 3A with the following changes: the deductible is $250, the copayment is 15%, and the maximum yearly copayment is $700. Suppose a policy owner acquires a medical bill of $1250.
a) How much of the bill is the policy owner responsible for?
b) How much will the insurance company be responsible for?

Solutions:
3A) a) $493.75; **b)** $1,031.25
3B) a) $400; **b)** $850

EXAMPLE 4:

4A) Consider the graphs that accompany Example 4 on pages 12-13 of your text. Use the graphs to solve the following problems. **a)** Using the graph in Figure 1.1, estimate the world-wide e-commerce sales in 2000. **b)** Using the graph in Figure 1.1, estimate the worldwide e-commerce sales in 2004. Then use this estimate and Figure 1.2 to estimate the e-commerce sales in 2004 from Western Europe.

4B) Refer to Exercise 24 on page 17 of your text. Use the chart to solve the following problems. **a)** How many women enlisted in the Marine Corps? **b)** Determine approximately how many more women enlisted in the Air Force than in the Marine Corps.

Solutions:
4A) a) $0.8 trillion; **b)** $7 trillion; $1.582 trillion
4B) a) 4,580 women; **b)** 19,236 more women

EXAMPLE 5:

5A) Consider the graph that accompanies Example 5 on page 14 of your text. Use the graph to solve the following problems. **a)** Estimate the cost of 30-second commercials in 1970 and 2000. **b)** How much more was the cost for a 30-second commercial in 2000 than in 1970? **c)** How many times greater was the cost of a 30-second commercial in 2000 than in 1970?

5B) Consider Exercise 28 on page 18 of your text. Using the line graph provided, determine the approximate difference in the cost of electricity for a family that used 2000 kilowatt hours of electricity in October, 1999 versus October, 2000, if they received their electricity from Pacific Gas & Electric Company.

Solutions:
5A) a) $0.4 million in 1970, $2.3 million in 2000; **b)** $1.9 million; **c)** 5.75 times greater
5B) $120

EXAMPLE 6:

6A) Jennifer Louis' first five exam grades are 92, 88, 85, 83, and 82.
a) Find the mean for Jennifer's five grades. **b)** If one more exam is to be given, what is the minimum grade that Jennifer can receive to obtain a B average (a mean average of 84 or better, but less than 92)? **c)** Is it possible for Jennifer to obtain an A average (92 or better)? Explain.

6B) Samuel has homework grades of 98, 92, 78, 78, 93, 76, and 80. **a)** Find the mean average for these seven homework grades. **b)** If Samuel has only one more homework grade for the class, is it possible for Samuel to obtain a B+ homework average (87 or better)? Explain. **c)** If one more homework grade is to be given, what is the minimum that Samuel can receive to obtain a C+ average (82 or better)?

Solutions:

6A) a) 86; **b)** 74; **c)** No, she will need to get a 122 on her next exam which is impossible.

6B) a) 85; **b)** No, he will need to get a 101 on his next homework assignment, which is impossible. **c)** 61

Section 1.3

EXAMPLE 1:

1A) Bill has $\frac{1}{2}$ cup of flour. A recipe calls for 2 cups of flour. How many additional cups does he need?

1B) Janine has run 3.5 miles. She needs to run a total of 10 miles. How many additional miles does she need to run?

Solutions:

1A) $1\frac{1}{2}$ cups   **1B)** 6.5 miles

EXAMPLE 2:

Simplify

2A) $\frac{32}{48}$ **2B)** $\frac{24}{28}$

2C) $\frac{12}{36}$ **2D)** $\frac{36}{72}$

Solutions:

2A) $\frac{2}{3}$ **2B)** $\frac{6}{7}$

2C) $\frac{1}{3}$ **2D)** $\frac{1}{2}$

EXAMPLE 3:

Multiply.

3A) $\frac{9}{13}$ by $\frac{3}{8}$ **3B)** $\frac{7}{11}$ by $\frac{5}{13}$

Solutions:

3A) $\frac{27}{104}$ **3B)** $\frac{35}{143}$

EXAMPLE 4:

Multiply.

4A) $\frac{4}{15} \cdot \frac{5}{8}$ **4B)** $\frac{4}{12} \cdot \frac{6}{20}$

4C) $\frac{24}{10} \cdot \frac{7}{12}$ **4D)** $\frac{36}{15} \cdot \frac{45}{20}$

Solutions:

4A) $\frac{1}{6}$ **4B)** $\frac{1}{10}$

4C) $\frac{7}{5}$ **4D)** $\frac{27}{5}$

EXAMPLE 5:

Multiply.

5A) A snow blower engine runs on a mixture of gas and oil. One particular snow blower engine requires a mixture of $\frac{7}{16}$ quart of oil for each quart of gasoline used. If one wishes to make a mixture for this engine using 8 gallons of gasoline, how much oil must be used?

5B) A certain recipe calls for 1 egg and $\frac{2}{3}$ cup of white sugar. If one has five eggs, and would like to use them all in this recipe, how much sugar is needed?

Solutions:

5A) 3.5 quarts of oil

5B) $3\frac{1}{3}$ cup of sugar

EXAMPLE 6:

Divide.

6A) $\frac{4}{7} \div \frac{7}{8}$ **6B)** $\frac{9}{5} \div \frac{9}{2}$

6C) $\frac{7}{10} \div 8$ **6D)** $\frac{6}{8} \div 4$

Solutions:

6A) $\frac{32}{49}$ **6B)** $\frac{2}{5}$

6C) $\frac{7}{80}$ **6D)** $\frac{3}{16}$

EXAMPLE 7

Add.

7A) $\frac{3}{12} + \frac{8}{12}$ **7B)** $\frac{6}{8} + \frac{1}{8}$

7C) $\frac{10}{17} - \frac{5}{17}$ **7D)** $\frac{6}{13} - \frac{4}{13}$

Solutions:

7A) $\frac{11}{12}$ **7B)** $\frac{7}{8}$

7C) $\frac{5}{17}$ **7D)** $\frac{2}{13}$

EXAMPLE 8:

Add.

8A) $\frac{1}{7} + \frac{1}{9}$ **8B)** $\frac{1}{3} + \frac{1}{5}$

Solutions:

8A) $\frac{16}{63}$ **8B)** $\frac{8}{15}$

EXAMPLE 9:

9A) How much larger is $\frac{7}{8}$ foot than $\frac{1}{6}$ foot?

9B) How much larger is $\frac{1}{3}$ yard than $\frac{1}{8}$ yard?

Solutions:

9A) $\frac{17}{24}$ foot   **9B)** $\frac{5}{24}$ yard

EXAMPLE 10:

10A) Change $4\frac{3}{8}$ to a fraction.

10B) Change $6\frac{5}{7}$ to a fraction.

Solutions:

10B) $\frac{35}{8}$ **10B)** $\frac{47}{7}$

EXAMPLE 11:

11A) Change $\frac{63}{8}$ to a mixed number.

11B) Change $^{35}/_4$ to a mixed number.
Solutions:
11A) $7\,^7/_8$ **11B)** $8\,^3/_4$

EXAMPLE 12:
12A) To repair an electrical wire, a $^3/_4$ inch piece of wire is added to a piece of wire that is $22\,^7/_8$ inches long. How long is the combined length?
12B) To extend the fence in his back yard, Vincent adds $6\,^2/_3$ feet of fencing to the existing $50\,^3/_4$ foot-long fence. How long is the combined length?
Solutions:
12A) $23\,^5/_8$ inches

12B) $57\,^5/_{12}$ feet

EXAMPLE 13:
13A) Baby Alex was $22\,^3/_8$ inches long at birth. At 9 months, Alex has growth to a length of $30\,^1/_4$ inches. How much has Alex grown in his first 9 months?
13B) Ronald decided to begin a running program in January. At this point he could average $2\,^1/_4$ miles of continuous running. After 6 months, Ronald was averaging $3\,^2/_3$ miles of continuous running. By how many miles of continuous running has Ronald improved in 6 months?
Solutions:
13A) $7\,^7/_8$ inches

13B) $1\,^5/_{12}$ miles

EXAMPLE 14:
14A) A rectangular piece of material 4 feet wide by $14\,^1/_4$ feet long is cut into 6 equal strips along the width (as in Example 14, page 27 of text). Find the dimensions of each strip.
14B) A plot of land 2 miles wide by $8\,^5/_8$ miles long is divided evenly into 3 subplots. It is divided along the width of the plot. Find the dimensions of each subplot.
Solutions:
14A) $4 \times 2\,^3/_{16}$ feet

14B) $2 \times 2\,^7/_8$ miles

Section 1.4
EXAMPLE 1:
Consider the following sets of numbers. List the elements in each set that are **a)** natural numbers, **b)** whole numbers, **c)** integers, **d)** rational numbers, **e)** irrational numbers, **f)** real numbers.
1A)
$$\left\{-6, -\frac{3}{4}, \sqrt{5}, -.8, 4, 0, 9.2, 5\frac{5}{8}, -\sqrt{8}\right\}$$

1B)
$$\left\{5.2, -\sqrt{13}, 0.23, 6, -\frac{7}{4}, 0, 7\frac{1}{9}, \sqrt{25}\right\}$$

Solutions:
1A) a) 4 ; **b)** $0, 4$; **c)** $-6, 0, 4$;
d) $-6, -.8, -\frac{3}{4}, 0, 4, 5\frac{5}{8}, 9.2$;
e) $-\sqrt{8}, \sqrt{5}$
1B) a) $\sqrt{25}, 6$; **b)** $0, \sqrt{25}, 6$;
c) $0, \sqrt{25}, 6$;
d) $-\frac{7}{4}, 0, 0.23, \sqrt{25}, 5.2, 6, 7\frac{1}{9}$
e) $-\sqrt{13}$

Section 1.5
EXAMPLE 1:
Insert either > or < in the blank provided to make a true statement.
1A) -5 __ -1   **1B)** $-\frac{5}{2}$ __ 1.5
1C) $\frac{1}{5}$ __ $\frac{1}{6}$ **1D)** -3 __ 5
1E) $-\frac{3}{8}$ __ $-\frac{5}{7}$
1F) -1.1 __ -1.2
Solutions:
1A) <   **1B)** <
1C) >   **1D)** <
1E) >   **1F)** >

EXAMPLE 2:
Insert either > or < in the blank provided to make a true statement.
2A) -2 __ -4
2B) 0 __ -3
2C) -3 __ 3
2D) -5.2 __ -5.02
Solutions:
2A) >   **2B)** >
2C) <   **2D)** <

EXAMPLE 3:
Insert either >, <, or = in the blank provided to make a true statement.
3A) 5 __ |5|
3B) |3| __ |-3|
3C) -5 __ |-6|
3D) |-19| __ |15|
3E) -|4| __ |-4|
3F) |3| __ -|5|
3G) 0 __ |-9|
3H) $|-14|$ __ $\left|\dfrac{10}{3}\right|$
Solutions:
3A) =   **3B)** =
3C) <   **3D)** >
3E) <   **3F)** >
3G) <   **3H)** >

Section 1.6
EXAMPLE 1:
Evaluate using a number line.
3A) 5 + (-3)   **3B)** 9 + (-12)

Solutions:
3A) 2   **3B)** -3

EXAMPLE 2:
Evaluate using a number line.
2A) −7 + 3   **2B)** −4 + 8
Solutions:
2A) −4   **2B)** 4

EXAMPLE 3:
Evaluate using a number line.
3A) −2 + (-5)   **3B)** -5 + (-1)
Solutions:
3A) −7   **3B)** -6

EXAMPLE 4:
Add using a number line.
4A) 4 + (-4)   **4B)** (-10) + 10
Solutions:
4A) 0   **4B)** 0

EXAMPLE 5:
5A) A miner descends 120 feet in a mineshaft. Later he descends another 145 feet. Find the depth of the miner.
5B) A submarine dives 101 meters. Later it ascends 25 meters. Find the depth of the submarine.
Solutions:
5A) -265 feet   **5B)** -76 meters

EXAMPLE 6:
Add.
6A) $-\dfrac{7}{12}+\dfrac{2}{5}$ **6B)** $\dfrac{5}{8}+\left(-\dfrac{6}{7}\right)$

Solutions:
6A) $-\dfrac{11}{60}$ **6B)** $-\dfrac{13}{56}$

EXAMPLE 7:
Add.
7A) $-\dfrac{5}{6}+\left(-\dfrac{3}{4}\right)$

7B) $-\dfrac{1}{8}+\left(-\dfrac{8}{11}\right)$

Solutions:
7A) $-\dfrac{19}{12}$ **7B)** $-\dfrac{75}{88}$

EXAMPLE 8:
Find the opposite of each number.
8A) 5   **8B)** −4

8C) $-\dfrac{2}{7}$ **8D)** $\dfrac{11}{5}$

Solutions:
8A) −5   **8B)** 4

8C) $\dfrac{2}{7}$ **8D)** $-\dfrac{11}{5}$

EXAMPLE 9:
Add.
9A) 34 + 5   **9B)** 12 + 7
Solutions:
9A) 39   **9B)** 19

EXAMPLE 10:
Add.
10A) −5 + (-10)
10B) −17 + (-5)
Solutions:
10A) −15   **10B)** -22

EXAMPLE 11:
Add.
11A) 12 + (-10)   **11B)** (-5) + 13
Solutions:
11A) 2   **11B)** 8

EXAMPLE 12:
Add.
12A) 14 + (-19)
12B) 20 + (-15)
Solutions:
12A) −5   **12B)** 5

EXAMPLE 13:
Add.
13A) −23 + 26   **13B)** −13 + 10
Solutions:
13A) 3   **13B)** -3

EXAMPLE 14:
Add.
14A) $-\dfrac{2}{5}+\dfrac{3}{7}$

14B) $\dfrac{3}{4}+\left(-\dfrac{4}{9}\right)$

Solutions:

14A) $\dfrac{1}{35}$ **14B)** $\dfrac{11}{36}$

EXAMPLE 15:
Add.
15A) −17.56 + (-19.23)
15B) −12.92 + 15.67
Solutions:
15A) 36.79   **15B)** 2.75

EXAMPLE 16:
16A) The McNeal Bakery Corporation has a profit of $450,567 for the first five months of the year, and a loss of $52,987 for the remainder of the year. Find the net profit or loss for the year.
16B) The temperature (in Fahrenheit) at 8:30 a.m. was 4°. By 10:45 a.m., the temperature dropped to 12° below zero. Find the temperature change from 8:30 a.m. to 10:45 a.m.
Solutions:
16A) $397,580 profit
16B) 16° F

Section 1.7
EXAMPLE 1:
Evaluate by changing the expression to a sum.
1A) 8 − (+3)   **1B)** 9 − (+6)
Solutions:
1A) 5   **1B)** 3

EXAMPLE 2:
Evaluate by changing the expression to a sum.
2A) 6 − 2   **2B)** 10 − 3
Solutions:
2A) 4   **2B)** 7

EXAMPLE 3:
Evaluate by changing the expression to a sum.
3A) 5 − 8   **3A)** 7 − 10
3C) −9 − 4   **3D)** −11 - 13
Solutions:
3A) −3   **3B)** −3
3C) −13   **3D)** -24

EXAMPLE 4:
Evaluate by changing the expression to a sum.
4A) 9 − (-4)   **4B)** 15 − (-19)

Solutions:
4A) 13   **4B)** 34

EXAMPLE 5:
Evaluate by changing the expression to a sum.
5A) $6 - (-5)$ **5B)** $7 - (-17)$
5C) $-16 - (-19)$ **5D)** $-24 - (-2)$
Solutions:
5A) 11   **5B)** 24
5C) 3   **5D)** -22

EXAMPLE 6:
6A) Subtract 16 from 5.
6B) Subtract 18 from 20.
Solutions:
6A) -11 **6B)** 2

EXAMPLE 7:
7A) Subtract 6 from 6.
7B) Subtract 33 from 33.
Solutions:
7A) 0   **7B)** 0

EXAMPLE 8:
8A) Subtract -7.38 from 3.59.
8B) Subtract 9.25 from (-3.71).
Solutions:
8A) 10.97   **8B)** -12.96

EXAMPLE 9:
Subtract.
9A) $\dfrac{5}{8} - \dfrac{19}{20}$ **9B)** $\dfrac{7}{9} - \dfrac{9}{10}$
Solutions:
9A) $-\dfrac{13}{40}$ **9B)** $-\dfrac{11}{90}$

EXAMPLE 10:
Subtract.
10A) $-\dfrac{8}{17} - \dfrac{2}{3}$ **10B)** $-\dfrac{5}{13} - \dfrac{3}{5}$
Solutions:
10A) $-\dfrac{58}{51}$ **10B)** $-\dfrac{64}{65}$

EXAMPLE 11:
11A) Tim Downing's checkbook indicated a balance of $567.23 before he wrote a check for $250.69. Find the balance in his checkbook.

11B) Mary Martin has a balance in her checkbook of $500. She must write a check for $550 for rent. Her bank charges her $25 for each check that causes her checking account balance to fall below $0. Find the balance in Mary's checkbook after this check clears the bank. (Assume she makes no deposits before this happens.)
Solutions:
11A) $316.54   **11B)** -$75

EXAMPLE 12:
12A) On January 10, 1999, the high temperature for in day in Fargo, North Dakota was -5°F. On the same day, the high temperature in Dallas, Texas was 64°F. Find the difference in their temperatures.
12B) On a particular January day, the low temperature in Wistler, British Columbia was -25°F. On the same day, the low temperature in St. Paul, Minnesota was -10°F. Find the difference in their temperatures.
Solutions:
12A) 69°F   **12B)** 15°F

EXAMPLE 13
13A) Suppose Bill Rickets has a board that measures $2\,^5\!/_{16}$ feet. He knows that in order to be able to use the board for his project, he must cut $^3\!/_8$ foot from the board. What will the length of the board be once Bill makes this cut?
13B) Jane purchases a new pair of pants whose inseam is 32 ½ inches long. In order to hem the pants, Jane must cut 2 ¾ inches from the pants. What will the inseam of the pants be once Jane makes this cut?
Solutions:

13A) $1\,^{15}\!/_{16}$ feet

13B) $29\,^3\!/_4$ inches

EXAMPLE 14:
Evaluate:
14A) $17 + (-9)$
14B) $26 + (-15)$
14C) $-17 - 9$
14D) $-29 - 23$
14E) $14 + (-15)$
14F) $18 + (-31)$
14G) $9 - (-3)$
14H) $10 - (-14)$
14I) $-11 - (-2)$
14J) $-3 - (-7)$
14K) $6 - 19$
14L) $5 - 29$
Solutions:
14A) 8   **14B)** 11
14C) -26   **14D)** -52
14E) -1   **14F)** -13
14G) 12   **14H)** 24
14I) -9 **14J)** 4
14K) -13 **14L)** -24

EXAMPLE 15:
Evaluate mentally.
15A) $-10 - 9$ **15B)** $-6 - 15$
15C) $17 - 27$ **15D)** $34 - 14$
15E) $-21 - 13$ **15F)** $-30 - 15$
Solutions:
15A) -19 **15B)** -21
15C) -10 **15D)** 20
15E) -34 **15F)** -45

EXAMPLE 16:
Evaluate.
16A) $-\dfrac{2}{7} - \dfrac{4}{5}$ **16B)** $-\dfrac{2}{3} - \dfrac{5}{6}$
Solutions:
16A) $-\dfrac{38}{35}$ **16B)** $-\dfrac{3}{2}$

EXAMPLE 17:
Evaluate.
17A) $-6 - 14 - 7$
17B) $-9 - 10 - 13$
17C) $-4 + 1 - 10$
17D) $5 - 9 - 23$
17E) $10 - 9 + 4$
17F) $12 - 14 + 6$
Solutions:
17A) -27 **17B)** -32
17C) -13 **17D)** -27
17E) 5   **17F)** 4

EXAMPLE 18:
Evaluate. Then simplify the expression. Finally evaluate the simplified expression.
18A) $-7 - (-3) + (-13) + (-2)$
18B) $41 - (-6) + (-5) - (-32)$
Solutions:
18A) -19; $-7 + 3 - 13 - 2$;
-19
18B) 74; $41 + 6 - 5 + 32$; 74

Section 1.8

EXAMPLE 1:
Evaluate.
1A) $4(-9)$ **1B)** $5(-10)$
1C) $(-3)(2)$ **1D)** $(-4)(2)$
1E) $(-8)(-4)$ **1F)** $(-7)(-3)$
Solutions:
1A) -36 **1B)** -50
1C) -6 **1D)** -8
1E) 32 **1F)** 21

EXAMPLE 2:
Evaluate.
2A) $(-5)(9)$ **2B)** $(-2)(10)$
2C) $(-7)(-3)$ **2D)** $(-10)(-2)$
2E) $9(-7)$ **2F)** $4(-9)$
2G) $0(5)$ **2H)** $9(0)$
2I) $0(-3)$ **2J)** $(-4)0$
2K) $-4(-7)$ **2L)** $-6(-4)$
Solutions:
2A) -45 **2B)** -20
2C) 21 **2D)** 20
2E) -63 **2F)** -36
2G) 0 **2H)** 0
2I) 0 **2J)** 0
2K) 28 **2L)** 24

EXAMPLE 3:
Evaluate
3A) $\left(\dfrac{-1}{6}\right) \bullet \left(\dfrac{-4}{7}\right)$

3B) $\left(\dfrac{-2}{7}\right) \bullet \left(\dfrac{-3}{5}\right)$

3C) $\left(\dfrac{4}{30}\right) \bullet \left(\dfrac{-4}{15}\right)$

3D) $\left(\dfrac{-3}{4}\right) \bullet \left(\dfrac{3}{7}\right)$

Solutions:

3A) $\dfrac{2}{21}$ **3B)** $\dfrac{6}{35}$

3C) $-\dfrac{8}{225}$ **3D)** $-\dfrac{9}{28}$

EXAMPLE 4:
Evaluate.
4A) $(-3)(4)(-9)(-3)$
4B) $(6)(-9)(3)(-2)$
4C) $(-2)(-1)(4)(-5)(-2)$
4D) $(-3)(-9)(2)(5)(-3)$
Solutions:
4A) -324 **4B)** 324
4C) 80 **4D)** -810

EXAMPLE 5:
Evaluate
5A) $\dfrac{8}{-2}$ **5B)** $\dfrac{12}{-4}$

5C) $\dfrac{-36}{4}$ **5D)** $\dfrac{-12}{3}$

5E) $\dfrac{-36}{-9}$ **5F)** $\dfrac{-45}{-9}$

Solutions:
5A) -4 **5B)** -3
5C) -9 **5D)** -4
5E) 4 -   **5F)** 5

EXAMPLE 6:
Evaluate.
6A) $-18 \div (-3)$

6B) $-56 \div (-8)$

Solutions:
6A) 6 **6B)** 7

EXAMPLE 7:
Evaluate.
7A) $\dfrac{3}{4} \div \dfrac{-2}{5}$ **7B)** $\dfrac{-2}{3} \div \dfrac{3}{5}$

Solutions:
7A) $-\dfrac{15}{8}$ **7B)** $-\dfrac{10}{9}$

EXAMPLE 8:
Indicate whether each quotient is 0 or undefined.
8A) $\dfrac{0}{6}$ **8B)** $\dfrac{2}{0}$

8C) $\dfrac{0}{-2}$ **8D)** $\dfrac{-9}{0}$

Solution:
8A) 0 **8B)** undefined
8C) 0 **8D)** undefined

Section 1.9

EXAMPLE 1:
Evaluate.
1A) 6^2 **1B)** 9^2
1C) 2^3 **1D)** 3^4
1E) 1^4 **1F)** 1^{99}
1G) $(-5)^2$ **1H)** $(-12)^2$
1I) $(-5)^3$ **1J)** $(-7)^3$
1K) $\left(\dfrac{3}{5}\right)^2$ **1L)** $\left(\dfrac{2}{5}\right)^2$

Solutions:
1A) 36 **1B)** 81
1C) 8 **1D)** 81
1E) 1 **1F)** 1
1G) 25 **1H)** 144
1I) -125 **1J)** -343
1K) $\dfrac{9}{25}$ **1L)** $\dfrac{4}{25}$

EXAMPLE 2:
Evaluate.
1A) -9^2 **1B)** -10^2
1C) $(-10)^2$ **1D)** $(-11)^2$
1E) -5^3 **1F)** -4^3
Solutions:
1A) -81 **1B)** -100
1C) 100 **1D)** 121
1E) -125 **1F)** -64

EXAMPLE 3:
Evaluate.
3A) -2^6 **3B)** -3^4
3C) $(-2)^6$ **3D)** $(-3)^4$
Solutions:
3A) -64 **3B)** -81
3C) 64 **3D)** 81

EXAMPLE 4:
Evaluate.
4A) $3 + 2 \bullet 4^2 - 8$
4B) $6 + 3 \bullet 3^2 - 10$
Solutions:
4A) 27 **4B)** 23

EXAMPLE 5:
Evaluate.
5A) $7 + 2\left[\left(36 \div 3^2\right) + 6\right]$

5B) $2 + 4\left[\left(12 \div 2^2\right) + 8\right]$

5A) 27   **5B)** 46

EXAMPLE 6:
Evaluate.

6A) $(8 \div 2) + 3(6-4)^2$

6B) $(14 \div 2) + 5(3-2)^2$

Solutions:
6A) 16   **6B)** 12

EXAMPLE 7:
Evaluate.

7A) $-9 - 72 \div 8 \bullet 3^2 + 5$

7B) $-7 - 56 \div 7 \bullet 2^2 + 4$

Solutions:
7A) -85 **7B)** -35

EXAMPLE 8:
Evaluate.

8A) $-3^2 + 10 \div 5$

8B) $-5^2 + 18 \div 3$

8C) $(-3)^2 + 10 \div 5$

8D) $(-5)^2 + 18 \div 3$

Solutions:
8A) -7 **8B)** -19
8C) 11   **8D)** 31

EXAMPLE 9:
Evaluate.

9A) $\dfrac{4}{7} - \dfrac{3}{5} \bullet \dfrac{1}{8}$ **9B)** $\dfrac{3}{5} - \dfrac{2}{3} \bullet \dfrac{1}{7}$

Solutions:
9A) $\dfrac{139}{280}$ **9B)** $\dfrac{53}{105}$

EXAMPLE 10:
Write the following statements as mathematical expressions using parenthesis and brackets and then evaluate.
10A) Subtract 6 from 16. Divide this difference by 5. Multiply this quotient by 5.
10B) Add 12 to 23. Multiply this sum by 2. Divide this product by 3.
Solutions:

10A) $5\left[(16-6) \div 5\right]; 25$

10B) $\left[(12+23) \bullet 2\right] \div 3; \dfrac{70}{3}$

EXAMPLE 11:
11A) Evaluate 6x – 3 when x = 5.
11B) Evaluate 7x + 9 when x = 2.
Solutions:
11A) 27   **11B)** 23

EXAMPLE 12:
Evaluate x^2 and $-x^2$ when
12A) x = 8   **12B)** x = 4
Solutions:
12A) 64; -64   **12B)** 16, -16

EXAMPLE 13:
Evaluate y^2 and $-y^2$ when
13A) y = -7   **13B)** y = -2
Solutions:
13A) 49; -49   **13B)** 4; -4

EXAMPLE 14:
14A) Evaluate $(4x+2) + 3x^2$

when $x = \frac{1}{3}$.

14B) Evaluate $(3x+4) + 2x^2$

when $x = \frac{2}{3}$.

Solutions:

14A) $\dfrac{11}{3}$ **14B)** $\dfrac{62}{9}$

EXAMPLE 15:
15A) Evaluate $4(y+4) - x^2 - 7$
when x = -2 and y = -3.
15B) Evaluate $2(x+1) - y^2 + 9$
when x = -1 and y = -2.
Solutions:
15A) -7 **15B)** 5

Section 1.10
EXAMPLE 1:
Name each property illustrated.
1A) –3 + (-5) = -5 + (-3)
1B) 6 + 10 = 10 + 6
1C) 6(x – 9) = 6x - 54
1D) (5 + w)2 = 5 • 2 + w • 2
1E) $5 \bullet x = x \bullet 5$
1F) rg = gr
1G) (m + n) + 5 = m + (n + 5)
1H) 6 + (w + 1) = (6 + w) + 1

Solutions:
1A) Commutative property of addition
1B) Commutative property of addition
1C) Distributive property
1D) Distributive property
1E) Commutative property of multiplication
1F) Commutative property of multiplication
1G) Associative property of addition
1H) Associative property of addition

EXAMPLE 2:
Name each property illustrated.
2A) $3(y+2) = 3y + 6$
2B) $(a-12)c = ac - 12c$
2C) $2 + (m+n) = (2+m) + n$
2D) $4 \bullet (7 \bullet 8) = (4 \bullet 7) \bullet 8$
2E) $(3 \bullet 4)5 = 3(4 \bullet 5)$
2F) $\dfrac{1}{6} \bullet 6 = 1$
2G) $2 \bullet 0.5 = 1$
2H) $-5x + 5x = 0$
2I) $0 = 64 + (-64)$
2J) $-3x + 0 = -3x$
2K) $0 + 9t = 9t$
2L) $4p \bullet 1 = 4p$
Solutions:
2A) Distributive property
2B) Distributive property
2C) Associative property of addition
2D) Associative Property of multiplication
2E) Associative Property of multiplication
2F) Inverse Property of multiplication
2G) Inverse Property of multiplication
2H) Inverse Property of addition
2I) Inverse Property of addition
2J) Identity Property of addition
2K) Identity Property of addition
2L) Identity Property of addition

Chapter 2: Solving Linear Equations and Inequalities

Section 2.1

EXAMPLE 1:
Identify any like terms.
1A) $8 + 4y + 3y$
1B) $4x + 6 + 5x$
1C) $6a + 2 + 5b$
1D) $6a + 6b + 5$
1E) $r + 5 - \frac{1}{3} + x$
1F) $a + 9 - \frac{1}{3}a + q$
1G) $6a^2 + 6a + 5a^2$
1H) $2x^2 + x^3 + 6x + \frac{x^3}{6}$
Solutions:
1A) $4y$ and $3y$ are like terms .
1B) $4x$ and $5x$ are like terms .
1C) There are no like terms.
1D) There are no like terms.
1E) 5 and $-\frac{1}{3}$ are like terms .
1F) a and $-\frac{1}{3}a$ are like terms .
1G) $6a^2$ and $5a^2$ are like terms .
1H) $2x^3$ and $\frac{x^3}{6}$ are like terms .

EXAMPLE 2:
Identify any like terms.
1A) $7y - 4y + 3$
1B) $12 - a + 2a$
1C) $2 + 12a - 3 + -4a$
1D) $3x - 1 - 22x + 4$
1E) $5x^2 + 14 - 2x + 4$
1F) $4 - 4x^2 - 3x + 9x^2$
Solutions:
1A) $7y$ and $-4y$ are like terms .
1B) $-a$ and $-2a$ are like terms .
1C) 2 and -3 are like terms;
  $12a$ and $-4a$ are like terms .

1D) $3x$ and $-22x$ are like terms;
  -1 and 4 are like terms.
1E) 14 and 4 are like terms.
1F) $-4x^2$ and $9x^2$ are like terms .

EXAMPLE 3:
Combine like terms.
3A) $6x + 7x$ **3B)** $6a + 12a$
Solutions:
3A) $13x$ **3B)** $18a$

EXAMPLE 4:
Combine like terms.
4A) $\frac{2}{3}x - \frac{4}{5}x$ **4B)** $\frac{3}{4}a - \frac{6}{11}a$
Solutions:
4A) $-\frac{2}{15}x$ **4B)** $\frac{9}{44}a$

EXAMPLE 5:
Combine like terms.
5A) $3.72b - 8.12b$
5B) $9.25x - 8.75x$
Solutions:
5A) $-4.4b$ **5B)** $0.5x$

EXAMPLE 6:
Combine like terms.
6A) $2x + x + 10$
6B) $6x + 12 + 10x$
Solutions:
6A) $3x + 10$ **6B)** $16x + 12$

EXAMPLE 7:
Combine like terms.
7A) $5x + 7y - 2x - 5$
7B) $7b + 9c - 12 + 5c$
Solutions:
7A) $3x + 7y - 5$
7B) $7b + 14c - 12$

EXAMPLE 8:
Combine like terms.
8A) $-4y + 2x - 6y + 4 - x + 7$
8B) $7a - 3b + 8a - 12 + 4 - 12b$
Solutions:
8A) $-10y + x + 11$
8B) $15a - 15b - 8$

EXAMPLE 9:
Use the distributive property to remove parenthesis.
9A) $3(x + 2)$ **9B)** $5(y + 3)$
9C) $-3(r + 10)$ **9D)** $-6(y + 2)$
Solutions:
9A) $3x + 6$ **9B)** $5y + 15$
9C) $-3r - 30$ **9D)** $-6y - 12$

EXAMPLE 10:
Use the distributive property to remove parenthesis.
10A) $4(x - 8)$
10B) $8(w - 7)$
10C) $-3(r - 9)$
10D) $-5(y - 2)$
Solutions:
10A) $4x - 32$
10B) $8w - 56$
10C) $-3r + 27$
10D) $-5y + 10$

EXAMPLE 11:
Use the distributive property to remove parenthesis.
11A) $8(x - 9)$
11B) $-3(4r - 6)$
11C) $-5(2x - 3)$
11D) $-\frac{2}{3}(5t + 6)$
11E) $-\frac{1}{2}(3x - 6)$
11F) $-4(2x + 3y - 5z)$
11G) $-2(6a - b - 4c)$
Solutions:
11A) $8x - 72$
11B) $-12r + 18$
11C) $-10x + 15$
11D) $-\frac{10}{3}t - 4$
11E) $-\frac{3}{2}x + 3$
11F) $-8x - 12y + 20z$
11G) $-12a + 2b + 8c$

EXAMPLE 12:
Use the distributive property to remove parenthesis.
12A) $(3x - 9)5$ **12B)** $(9b - 1)6$

Solutions:
12A) $15x - 45$ **12B)** $54b - 6$

EXAMPLE 13:
Simplify.
13A) $7 - (3x + 4)$
13B) $10 - (6x + 12)$
Solutions:
13A) $3 - 3x$ **13B)** $-2 - 6x$

EXAMPLE 14:
Simplify.
14A) $-\left(\dfrac{3}{4}x - \dfrac{1}{3}\right) + 2x$
14B) $3x - \left(\dfrac{4}{5}x - \dfrac{2}{3}\right)$
Solutions:
14A) $\dfrac{5}{4}x + \dfrac{1}{3}$ **14B)** $\dfrac{11}{5}x + \dfrac{2}{3}$

EXAMPLE 15:
Simplify.
15A) $\dfrac{2}{3}x + \dfrac{1}{3}(5x - 4)$
15B) $\dfrac{3}{4}x + \dfrac{1}{2}(x - 5)$
Solutions:
15A) $\dfrac{7}{3}x - \dfrac{4}{3}$ **15B)** $\dfrac{5}{4}x - \dfrac{5}{2}$

EXAMPLE 16:
Simplify.
16A) $3(x - 5) - 2(x - 4) - 10$
16B) $9(b - 6) - 4 - 3(b - 5)$
Solutions:
16A) $x - 17$ **16B)** $6b - 43$

Section 2.2
EXAMPLE 1:
1A) Consider the equation
$5x - 2 = 18$. Determine whether
4 is a solution.
1B) Consider the equation
$6x - 5 = 25$. Determine
whether 3 is a solution.
Solutions:
1A) Yes   **1B)** No

EXAMPLE 2:
2A) Determine whether 35 is a
solution to the equation
$4x - 3(x - 5) = 50$.
2B) Determine whether 17 is a
solution to the equation
$2x - 5(x + 5) = 10$.
Solutions:
2A) Yes   **2B)** No

EXAMPLE 3:
3A) Determine whether $-\dfrac{1}{3}$ is
a solution to the equation
$21x = 3(x - 2)$.
3B) Determine whether $-\dfrac{2}{3}$ is
a solution to the equation
$-9x = 4(x + 5)$.
Solutions:
3A) Yes   **3B)** No

EXAMPLE 4:
Solve each equation.
4A) $x - 5 = -2$
4B) $a - 8 = -12$
Solutions:
4A) $x = 3$ **4B)** $a = -4$

EXAMPLE 5
Solve each equation.
5A) $z + 4 = 7$ **5B)** $t + 11 = 9$
Solutions:
5A) $z = 3$ **5B)** $t = -2$

EXAMPLE 6:
Solve each equation.
6A) $x + 7 = -10$
6B) $b + 10 = -5$
Solutions:
6A) $x = -17$ **6B)** $b = -15$

EXAMPLE 7:
Solve each equation.
7A) $8 = x - 7$ **7B)** $10 = b - 3$
Solutions:
7A) $x = 15$ **7B)** $b = 13$

EXAMPLE 8:
Solve each equation.
8A) $-8.75 = r + 13.25$
8B) $-5.65 = y + 6.75$

Solutions:
8A) $x = 22$ **8B)** $y = 12.4$

Section 2.3
EXAMPLE 1:
Solve each equation.
1A) $4x = 12$ **1B)** $5b = 65$
Solutions:
1A) $x = 3$ **1B)** $b = 13$

EXAMPLE 2:
Solve each equation.
2A) $\dfrac{x}{3} = 9$ **2B)** $\dfrac{r}{4} = 7$
Solutions:
2A) $x = 27$ **2B)** $r = 28$

EXAMPLE 3:
Solve each equation.
3A) $\dfrac{3}{4}x = 9$ **3B)** $\dfrac{2}{3}y = 12$
Solutions:
3A) $x = 12$ **3B)** $y = 18$

EXAMPLE 4:
Solve each equation.
4A) $8r = 15$ **4B)** $9x = 12$
Solutions:
4A) $r = \dfrac{15}{8}$ **4B)** $x = \dfrac{4}{3}$

EXAMPLE 5:
Solve each equation.
5A) $-16 = -4y$
5B) $-24 = -6w$
Solutions:
5A) $y = 4$ **5B)** $w = 4$

EXAMPLE 6:
Solve each equation.
6A) $0.25x = 1.50$
6B) $0.27r = 0.81$
Solutions:
6A) $x = 6$ **6B)** $r = 3$

EXAMPLE 7:
Solve each equation.
7A) $-4x = \dfrac{5}{8}$ **7A)** $\dfrac{4}{7} = -3x$

Solutions:

7A) $x = -\dfrac{5}{32}$ **7B)** $x = -\dfrac{4}{21}$

EXAMPLE 8:
Solve each equation.

8A) $-7 = -\dfrac{2}{5}x$

8B) $-\dfrac{2}{3}x = -8$

Solutions:

8A) $x = \dfrac{35}{2}$ **8B)** $x = 12$

EXAMPLE 9:
Solve each equation.

9A) $-y = 10$ **9B)** $34 = -r$

Solutions:

9A) $y = -10$ **9B)** $r = -34$

EXAMPLE 10:
Solve each equation.

10A) $-y = -7$

10B) $-19 = -g$

Solutions:

10A) $y = 7$ **10B)** $g = 19$

EXAMPLE 11:
Solve each equation.

11A) $-4x = -24$

11B) $-26 = -2r$

Solutions:

11A) $x = 6$ **11B)** $r = 13$

EXAMPLE 12:
Solve each equation.

12A) $\dfrac{1}{5}x = 20$ **12B)** $\dfrac{1}{3}x = 23$

Solutions:

12A) $x = 100$ **12B)** $x = 69$

Section 2.4

EXAMPLE 1:
Solve each equation.

1A) $3x - 7 = 11$

1B) $4x - 2 = -14$

Solutions:

1A) $x = 6$ **1B)** $x = -3$

EXAMPLE 2:
Solve each equation.

2A) $-2x - 9 = -8$

2B) $-3x - 4 = -2$

Solutions:

2A) $x = -\dfrac{1}{2}$ **2B)** $x = -\dfrac{2}{3}$

EXAMPLE 3:
Solve each equation.

3A) $14 = 5x + 8 - 3x$

3B) $6x - 3 + 3x = 15$

Solutions:

3A) $x = 3$ **3B)** $x = 2$

EXAMPLE 4:
Solve each equation.

4A) $3(x + 7) - 6x = -14$

4B) $9 = 2(x - 3) - 5x$

Solutions:

4A) $x = \dfrac{35}{3}$ **4B)** $x = -5$

EXAMPLE 5:
Solve each equation.

5A) $3y - (y + 5) = 9$

5B) $22 = 6x - (x - 3)$

Solutions:

5A) $y = 7$ **5B)** $x = \dfrac{19}{5}$

EXAMPLE 6:
Solve each equation.

6A) $0.91y + 2.25 - 0.01y = 5.85$

6B) $0.15 = 0.05x - 1.35 - 0.20x$

Solutions:

6A) $y = 4$ **6B)** $x = -10$

EXAMPLE 7:
Solve each equation.

7A) $\dfrac{x - 5}{3} = 8$ **7B)** $-9 = \dfrac{x + 7}{4}$

Solutions:

7A) $x = 29$ **7B)** $x = -43$

EXAMPLE 8:
Solve each equation.

8A) $\dfrac{r}{3} + 2r = 7$

8B) $23 = \dfrac{x}{4} - 6x$

Solutions:

8A) $r = 3$ **8B)** $x = -4$

EXAMPLE 9:
Solve each equation.

9A) $\dfrac{1}{3}x - \dfrac{3}{4}x = \dfrac{1}{5}$

9B) $\dfrac{1}{6} = \dfrac{1}{5}x - \dfrac{2}{7}x$

Solutions:

9A) $x = -\dfrac{12}{25}$ **9B)** $x = -\dfrac{35}{18}$

Section 2.5

EXAMPLE 1:
Solve each equation.

1A) $5x + 7 = 3x + 11$

1B) $4x - 10 = 5x - 15$

Solutions:

1A) $x = 2$ **1B)** $x = 5$

EXAMPLE 2:
Solve each equation.

2A) $4y - 2 - 8y = 19 + 5y - 3$

2B) $4x + 2 - 6x = 28 + 8x + 4$

Solutions:

2A) $y = -2$ **2B)** $x = -3$

EXAMPLE 3:
Solve each equation.

3A) $3(p + 2) = 5p - 18$

3B) $-5x + 5 = 5(x - 4)$

Solutions:

3A) $p = 12$ **3B)** $x = 2.5$

EXAMPLE 4:
Solve each equation.

4A) $3(x - 7) + 2 = 4x + 4$

4B) $5x = 2(x - 3) + 3$

Solutions:

4A) $x = -23$ **4B)** $x = -1$

EXAMPLE 5:
Solve each equation.

5A) $4 - 3x + 4x = -2(-4x + 5)$

5B) $-3(-2x + 7) = -2x - 3 - x$

Solutions:

5A) $x = 2$ **5B)** $x = 2$

EXAMPLE 6:
Solve each equation.
6A) $8.25x + 6.5 = 4.25x - 1.22$
6B) $3.22x + 7.92 = 2.3x + 6.08$

Solutions:
6A) $x = 1.93$ **6B)** $x = -2$

EXAMPLE 7:
Solve each equation.
7A) $\frac{1}{4}x = \frac{2}{3}x + \frac{1}{6}$

7B) $\frac{2}{5}x = \frac{1}{4}x + \frac{1}{7}$

Solutions:
7A) $x = -\frac{2}{5}$ **7B)** $x = \frac{20}{21}$

EXAMPLE 8:
Solve each equation.
8A) $\frac{x}{5} + 5 = 3(x - 3)$

8B) $2(x - 4) = \frac{x}{5} + 10$

Solutions:
8A) $x = 5$ **8B)** $x = 10$

EXAMPLE 9:
9A) $\frac{2}{5}(3x + 2) = \frac{1}{2}(x - 4) + 10$

9B) $\frac{1}{2}(x + 1) + 2 = \frac{3}{5}(5x + 2)$

Solutions:
9A) $x = \frac{88}{7}$ **9B)** $x = \frac{13}{25}$

EXAMPLE 10:
10A) $7x - 1 = 7\left(x - \frac{1}{7}\right)$

10B) $2(4x - 6) = 8x - 12$

Solutions:
10A) All real numbers
10B) All real numbers

EXAMPLE 11:
11A) $-2x + 5 + 3x = 5x - 4x + 7$
11B) $7x + 4 - 3x = -5x - 10 + 9x$
Solutions:
11A) No real solution
11B) No real solution

Section 2.6
EXAMPLE 1:
1A) Mr. Brown's tenth grade Algebra class recently took their 2nd exam. There were 6 A's, 13 B's, 6 C's, 4 D's, and 1 F. Find **a)** the ratio of the number of A's to the number of D's; **b)** the ratio of the number of C's to the total number of grades.
1B) Sally Strom was Sweet Valley's high scorer on the girls basketball team. She scored six 2-point baskets, three 3-point baskets, and 5 free-throws. Find **a)** the ratio of Sally's 2-point baskets to her 3-point baskets; **b)** the ratio of the points scored by Sally's 3-point baskets to the points scored by her free-throws.
Solutions:
1A) 3:2; 1:5   **1B)** 2:1; 9:5

EXAMPLE 2:
2A) The Golden Ratio is known to be approximately 1.6:1. This ratio is often used in design because of its aesthetic appeal. Suppose a rectangular section of a structure has the dimensions 60 feet by 45 feet. Do the dimensions of this section reflect the Golden Ratio?
2B) Suppose that a certain diet requires that one consume 3 servings of a carbohydrate-rich food for every 1 serving of fatty food. Suppose a person consumes 12.5 portions of carbohydrate-rich food and 4 servings of fatty food. Is this person approximately following the guidelines of the diet?
Solutions:
2A) No, 60:45 is equivalent to about 1.3:1
2B) Yes, 12.5:4 is approximately equivalent to 3:1

EXAMPLE 3:
3A) Suppose that a chainsaw requires a gas-oil mixture of 7 gallons of gasoline for every 48 ounces of oil. Find the ratio of gasoline to oil for this mixture.

3B) A certain recipe calls for 6 tablespoons of vinegar for every 1 cup of milk (to make buttermilk). Find the ratio of vinegar to milk in this mixture. (There are 16 tablespoons in 1 cup).
Solutions:
3A) 7:3   **3B)** 3:8

EXAMPLE 4:
Consider Example 4 on page 145 of your text. Refer to Figure 2.3.
4A) Find the gear ratio is the Driving gear has 72 teeth and the Driven gear has 16 teeth.
4B) Find the gear ratio is the Driven gear has 14 teeth and the Driving gear has 46 teeth.
Solutions:
4A) 9:2   **4B)** 23:7

EXAMPLE 5:
Solve for x by cross-multiplying.
5A) $\frac{x}{4} = \frac{42}{28}$ **5B)** $\frac{125}{25} = \frac{x}{5}$

Solutions:
5A) $x = 6$ **5B)** $x = 25$

EXAMPLE 6:
Solve for x by cross-multiplying.
6A) $\frac{-10}{4} = \frac{60}{x}$ **6B)** $\frac{3}{x} = \frac{12}{56}$

Solutions:
6A) $x = -24$ **6B)** $x = 14$

EXAMPLE 7:
7A) A 40-pound bag of fertilizer will cover an area of 350 square yards. **a)** Find the amount of fertilizer in pounds needed to cover an area of 8400 square yards. **b)** How many bags of fertilizer are needed?
7B) One 5-gallon bucket of paint will cover 750 square feet. **a)** How much paint in gallons in needed to cover 4200 square feet **b)** How many buckets of paint are needed?
Solutions:
7A) 960 pounds; 24 bags

7B) 28 gallons; approximately 6 buckets (5.6 exactly)

EXAMPLE 8:
8A) Mary Magney recently made a trip to her hometown from her college town. 300 miles of the trip is on an interstate. Thus, she can set the cruise control for this portion of the trip. In an effort to approximate the time of her trip, Mary measures that it takes 1 minute and 36 seconds to travel two miles. How long, in hours, will it take Mary to get home?
8B) Stan Packer wants to send fliers to persons in the area to advertise his new home business. He figures that he should send 5000 fliers. Before he can send the fliers, they must tri-folded. He times himself and finds that he can fold 10 fliers in 22 seconds. If Stan continues at this rate, how long will it take him to fold all of the fliers?
Solutions:
8A) 4 hours
8B) A little over three hours

EXAMPLE 9:
9A) A certain drug must be administered to a heart patient. A nurse must administer 220 milligrams of the drug to the patient. The drug is only available in a solution whose concentration in 50 miligrams of the drug per 0.9 milliliter of solution. How many milliliters of solution should the nurse administer?
9B) A doctor asks a nurse to give a patient 5.2 milliliters of a drug solution. If the solution has a concentration of 42 milligrams of the drug per 0.75 milliliter of solution, how many milligrams of the drug is administered to the patient?
Solutions:
9A) 3.96 milliliters
9B) 291.2 milligrams

EXAMPLE 10:
10A) There are 1760 yards in a mile. What it the distance, in miles, of 7920 feet?
10B) There are 1000 millimeters in a meter. What is the distance, in meters, of 13920 centimeters?
Solutions:
10A) 4.5 miles
10B) 139.2 meters

EXAMPLE 11:
11A) Suppose that the exchange rate from U.S. dollars to Mexican pesos is $1 per 10.567 pesos. **a)** How many pesos would one receive if he exchanged $200 U.S.? **b)** Find the cost in U.S. dollars of a leather purse purchased in Mexico, priced at 310 pesos.
11B) When M.C. Haynes visited Canada, she was able to exchange $145 Canadian for $100 U.S. If she exchanges another $700 Canadian for U.S. dollars, how much more in U.S. dollars will she receive?
Solutions:
11A) a) 2113.40 pesos;
b) $29.34
11B) $482.76

EXAMPLE 12:
Each pair of figures in 12A and 12B are similar. Find the length of the side indicated by the x.
12A)   12.5

EXAMPLE 13:
Each pair of triangles in parts 13A) and 13B) are similar. Use a proportion to find the length of the side indicated by x.
13A)

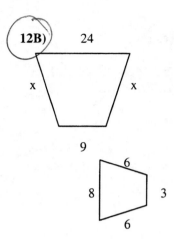

Solutions:
12A) x = 8.5   **12B)** x = 18

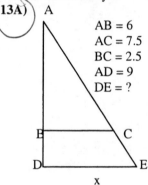

| AB = 6 |
| AC = 7.5 |
| BC = 2.5 |
| AD = 9 |
| DE = ? |

13B)

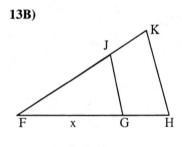

FH = 20.5
GJ = 8
KH = 10.25
FG = ?

Solutions:
13A) x = 3.75   **13B)** x = 16

Section 2.7

EXAMLE 1:
Solve each inequality and graph the solution on a number line.
1A) $x - 6 > 1$
1B) $x + 2 \le -2$
Solutions:
1A) $x > 7$ **1B)** $x \le -4$

EXAMPLE 2:
Solve each inequality and graph the solution on a number line.
2A) $3x + 7 \ge -2$
2B) $4x - 9 > 7$
Solutions:
2A) $x \ge -3$ **2B)** $x > 4$

EXAMPLE 3:
Multiply both sides of each inequality.
3A) $9 > -3$ by -3
3B) $-3 \le -4$ by -6
Solutions:
3A) $-27 < 9$ **3B)** $18 \ge 24$

EXAMPLE 4:
Divide both sides of each inequality.
4A) $10 > -20$ by -2
4B) $6 > 4$ by -2
Solutions:
4A) $-5 < 10$ **4B)** $-3 < -2$

EXAMPLE 5:
Solve each inequality and graph the solution on a number line.
5A) $-4x < 12$
5B) $-10x > -50$
Solutions:
5A) $x > -3$ **5B)** $x < 5$

EXAMPLE 6:
Solve each inequality two different ways. Then graph the solution on a number line.
6A) $6 \le -3 - x$
6B) $7 > -9 - x$
Solutions:
6A) $x \le -9$ **6B)** $x > -16$

EXAMPLE 7:
Solve each inequality and graph the solution on a number line.
7A) $-3p + 8 < -4p - 12$
7B) $6x - 2 \ge -2x + 14$
Solutions:
7A) $p < -20$ **7B)** $x \ge 2$

EXAMPLE 8:
Solve each inequality and graph the solution on a number line.

8A) $\dfrac{1}{4}x + 5 > -\dfrac{1}{5}x + 7$

8B) $-\dfrac{2}{3}x + 1 \le \dfrac{1}{4}x - 3$

Solutions:

8A) $x > \dfrac{40}{9}$ **8B)** $x \ge \dfrac{48}{11}$

EXAMPLE 9:
Solve each inequality and graph the solution on a number line.
9A) $3(x + 5) < 6x - 3x + 20$
9B) $9x - 12 - 7x \ge 2(x - 9)$
Solutions:
9A) All real numbers
9B) All real numbers

EXAMPLE 10:
Solve each inequality and graph the solution on a number line.
10A) $2x + 7 + 3x < 5(x + 1)$
10B) $9(x - 6) \le -x + 10x - 60$
Solutions:
10A) No solution
10B) No solution

Chapter 3: Formulas and Applications of Algebra

Section 3.1

EXAMPLE 1:
1A) In order to buy a car, Melanie Brown borrowed $7200 from a bank for 4 years. The bank charged 6% simple interest for the loan. How much interest will Melanie owe the bank?
1B) Greg Brody invests $2000 in a savings account for 2 years. The bank pays 7% simple interest per year. How much will Greg earn in two years?
Solutions:
1A) $1728   **1B)** $280

EXAMPLE 2:
2A) Jerry Simon invests $5000 in a savings account that earns simple interest for three years. If the interest earned from the account is $600, find the rate.
2B) Meg McGee takes out a loan for $4000 from a bank for 5 years. She does not want to pay more than $1000 interest for the loan. What is the largest annual interest rate must she secure to achieve this?
Solutions:
2A) 4%   **2B)** 5%

EXAMPLE 3:
3A) Donna Blanchard decides to fence in the back half of her backyard. This portion of her yard measures 35 feet long and 55 feet wide. **a)** How much fencing is needed? **b)** How large, in square feet, will the fenced area be?
3B) Jesus Hernandez wants to put fencing around his garden to keep the rabbits out. The dimensions of the garden are 26 feet and 18 feet. **a)** How much fencing is needed? **b)** How large, in square feet, will the fenced area be?
Solutions:
3A) 180 feet; 1925 square feet
3B) 88 feet; 468 square feet

EXAMPLE 4:
4A) George Snyder knows that the perimeter of his living room is 60 feet. He measures the width of the room and finds that it is 10 feet wide. Find the length of the room.
4B) Homer Hiles jogs a route that is rectangular in shape. He knows that one lap is 3.4 miles. He also knows that the length of the rectangular route is 1 mile. Find the width of the route.
Solutions:
4A) 20 feet   **4B)** 0.7 mile

EXAMPLE 5:
5A) The area of a trapezoidal plot of land is 4000 square feet. The bases of the trapezoidal plot are 150 feet and 50 feet. Find the distance between the bases of the trapezoidal plot.
5B) A decorative sidewalk is going to consist of parallelogram-shaped concrete slabs. It is known that each slab must cover an area of 32 square feet. The length of each slab is 8 feet and the width of each slab is 5 feet (see below).

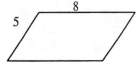

What must the height (the distance between the longer sides of the shape) of each slab be?
Solutions:
5A) 40 feet   **5B)** 4 feet

EXAMPLE 6:
6A) The Walters own a circular table. The diameter of the table is 270 centimeters. Find the circumference and area of the table.
6B) Tom Jennings owns a hot tub. He would like to build seating around the tub. He would also like to paint the bottom of the tub. The tub is circular in shape. The diameter of the tub is 6 feet. Find the circumference around the tub and the area of the bottom of the tub (the tub is a perfect cylinder).
Solutions:
6A) 270π cm; 18225π cm^2
6B) 6π feet; 9π square feet

EXAMPLE 7:
7A) The diameter of a basketball is approximately 8 inches. Find the approximate volume of the ball.
7B) The radius of a beach ball is 1.5 feet. Find the volume of the ball.
Solutions:
7A) 268.08 in^3 **7B)** 14.14 ft^3

EXAMPLE 8:
8A) A cylindrical garbage can has a volume of 12.6 cubic feet and a diameter of 2 feet. Find the height of the garbage can.
8B) A cylindrical grain silo has a volume of 35,342 cubic feet. The height of the silo is 50 feet. Find the diameter of the silo.
Solutions:
8A) Approximately 4 feet
8B) Approximately 30 feet

EXAMPLE 9:
The number of diagonals, d, in a polygon of n sides is given by the formula $d = \frac{1}{2}n^2 - \frac{3}{2}n$.
9A) How many diagonals does a dodecagon (12 sides) have?
9B) How many diagonals does a heptagon (7 sides) have?
Solutions:
9A) 54 diagonals
9B) 14 diagonals

EXAMPLE 10:
10A) The formula for the perimeter of an isosceles trapezoid (non-bases are equal in length) is $P = a + b + 2c$, where a and b are the lengths of the bases of the trapezoid. Solve this formula for c.
10B) The formula for the perimeter of a parallelogram can be written as $P = 2b + 2w$, where b is the base and w is the width. Solve this formula for b.
Solutions:

10A) $c = \dfrac{P - a - b}{2}$

10B) $b = \dfrac{P - 2w}{2}$

EXAMPLE 11:
11A) Solve the formula
$V = \frac{1}{3}bh$ for b.
11B) Solve the formula
$A = \frac{1}{2}h(a + b)$ for b.
Solutions:

11A) $b = \dfrac{3V}{h}$

11B) $b = \dfrac{2A}{h} - a$

EXAMPLE 12:
12A) Solve the equation 4x + 5y = 20 for y. Then find the value of y when x = 5.
12B) Solve the equation −3x − 4y = 12 for x. Then find the value of x when y = -6.
Solutions:

12A) $y = \dfrac{20 - 4x}{5}$; $y = 0$

12B) $x = \dfrac{-12 - 4y}{3}$; $x = 4$

EXAMPLE 13:
13A) Solve the formula
$P = \frac{1}{4}gt$ for g.

13B) Solve the formula
$G = \frac{3}{5}abc$ for c.
Solutions:

13A) $g = \dfrac{4P}{t}$ **13B)** $c = \dfrac{5G}{3ab}$

EXAMPLE 14:
14A) Solve the equation
$y - \frac{1}{5} = \frac{1}{3}(x - 2)$ for y.
14B) Solve the equation
$y + \frac{1}{5} = \frac{1}{7}(x + 1)$ for y.
Solutions:

14A) $y = \dfrac{1}{3}x - \dfrac{3}{5}$

14B) $y = \dfrac{1}{7}x - \dfrac{2}{35}$

Section 3.2
EXAMPLE 1:
Express each statement as an algebraic expression.
1A) The time, t, increased by 30 minutes.
1B) The sum of the distance, d, and 45 miles.
1C) Five less than twice the perimeter, P.
1D) The difference of three times the area, A, and 6.
1E) 3 ounces more than 10 times the weight, w.
1F) 22 more than 8 times the height.
1G) Three times the sum of the length, l, and 7.
1H) Four times the difference of x and y.
Solutions:
1A) $t + 30$ **1B)** $d + 45$
1C) $2P - 5$ **1D)** $3A - 6$
1E) $10w + 3$ **1F)** $22 + 8h$
1G) $3(l + 7)$ **1H)** $4(x - y)$

EXAMPLE 2:
Write three different statements to represent the following expressions.
2A) $4x + 3$ **2B)** $2 + 5x$

2C) $2x - 9$ **2D)** $11 - 6x$
Solutions:
2A)
1. Three more than 4 times a number.
2. Four times a number, increased by 3.
3. The sum of 4 times a number and 3.

2B)
1. Two more than five times a number.
2. Five times a number, increased by 2.
3. The sum of 2 and 5 times a number.

2C)
1. Nine less than 2 times a number.
2. Two times a number, less 9.
3. The difference between 2 times a number and 9.

2D)
1. Six times a number less than 11.
2. Eleven less 6 times a number.
3. The difference between 11 and 6 times a number.

EXAMPLE 3:
Write a statement to represent each expression.
3A) $4x - 5$ **3B)** $4(x - 5)$
3C) $3x + 7$ **3D)** $3(x + 7)$
Solutions:
3A) One possible answer: Four times a number less 5.
3B) One possible answer: Four times the difference of a number and 5.
3C) One possible answer: Three times a number increased by 7.
3D) Three times the sum of a number and 7.

EXAMPLE 4:
Express each phrase as an algebraic expression.
4A) The cost of a pair of jeans, p, decreased by 10%.

4B) The amount of an investment, A, increased by 5%.
4C) The population of a country, r, increased by 15%.
4D) One worker's annual salary, s, decreased by 2%.
Solutions:
4A) $p - 0.10p$ or $0.90p$
4B) $A + 0.05A$ or $1.05A$
4C) $r + 0.15r$ or $1.15r$
4D) $s - 0.02s$ or $0.98s$

EXAMPLE 5:
For each relationship, select a variable to represent one quantity and state what that quantity represents. Then express the second quantity in terms of the variable.
5A) The Rams scored 10 points less than the Tigers.
5B) Jonna is running 2.5 times faster than Rachel.
5C) Hank and Alice share $100.
5D) Sharon has 8 less than 3 times the amount that Jerry has.
5E) The width of a rectangle is 2 more than half the length.
5F) At Agriland, Inc., the average salary increased by 6% from 2002 to 2003.
5G) The profit of a business, in percent, is shared between two partners, Leona and Lisa.
Solutions:
5A) Let p be the number of points scored by the Tigers. Then $p - 10$ is the number of points scored by the Rams.
5B) Let r be Rachel's speed. Then $2.5r$ is Jonna's speed.
5C) Let h be the amount Hank receives. Then $100 - h$ is the amount that Alice receives.
5D) Let j be the amount that Jerry receives. Then $3j - 8$ is the amount that Sharon receives.
5E) Let l be the length. Then the width is $2 + \frac{1}{2}l$.
5F) Let s be the average salary in 2002. Then $s + 0.06s$

or $1.06s$ is the average salary in 2003.
5G) Let p be the amount that Leona receives. Then $100 - p$ is the amount that Lisa receives.

EXAMPLE 6:
Write each statement as an algebraic expression.
6A) The cost of purchasing n baseballs at $10 each.
6B) A 7% commission on s dollars in sales.
6C) The dollar amount earned in h hours if a person makes $9.92 per hour.
6D) The number of fat grams in x cookies if each cookie contains 2 grams of fat.
6E) The decrease in population in x years for a city shrinking by 15 persons per year.
6F) The distance traveled in t hours when 65 miles are traveled each hour.
Solutions:
6A) $10n$ dollars
6B) $0.07s$ dollars
6C) $9.92h$ dollars
6D) $2x$ grams
6E) $15x$ persons
6F) $65t$ miles

EXAMPLE 7:
7A) The cost for attending a local high school basketball game is $4.50 for adults and $2.50 for children. Write an algebraic expression to represent the total income received by the high school if x and y children attend the game.
7B) The Boy Scouts are selling tins of popcorn for a fundraising drive. The cost of a large tin is $15.75 and the cost of a small tin is $7.75. Write an algebraic expression to represent the total income received by the Boy Scouts if x large tins and y small tins are sold.
Solutions:
7A) $4.50x + 2.50y$ dollars

7B) $15.75x + 7.75y$ dollars

EXAMPLE 8:
Write an algebraic expression for each statement.
8A) The number of inches in x yards.
8B) The number of quarts in g gallons.
8C) The number of cents in q quarters and d dimes.
8D) The number of dollars in t ten-dollar bills and f five-dollar bills.
8E) The number of hours in w weeks, d days, and h hours.
8F) The number of millimeters in c centimeters and m millimeters.
Solutions:
8A) $36x$ inches
8B) $4g$ quarts
8C) $25q + 10d$ cents
8D) $10t + 5f$ dollars
8E) $168w + 24d + h$ hours
8F) $10c + m$ millimeters

EXAMPLE 9:
Write two statements to represent each equation.
9A) $x + 3 = 2x - 10$
9B) $4 - 3x = x - 1$
Solutions:
9A)
1. A number increased by 3 is ten less than two times a number.
2. The sum of a number and three is the difference between two times a number and ten.

9B)
1. The difference of 4 and 3 times a number is the difference of a number and 1.
2. Three times a number less than 4 is 1 less than a number.

EXAMPLE 10:
Write a statement to represent each equation.
10A) $x + 3(x - 5) = 4$
10B) $7(x - 2) = 6 - 2x$
Solutions:
10A) The sum of a number and three times the difference between the number and five is four.
10B) Seven times the difference of a number and 2 is the difference between 6 and twice a number.

EXAMPLE 11:
Write each problem as an equation.
11A) One number is 5 more than 4 times the other. Their sum is 20.
11B) A number is 3 more than 2 times another number. The difference of the numbers is 30.
11C) For two consecutive integers, the sum of the smaller and 5 times the larger is 40.
11D) For two consecutive even integers, the sum of the smaller and 4 times the larger is 58.
Solutions:
11A) $x + (4x + 5) = 20$
11B) $(2x + 3) - x = 30$
11C) $x + 5(x + 1) = 40$
11D) $x + 3(x + 2) = 58$

EXAMPLE 12:
Write the following problems as equations.
12A) One car travels 4 less than three times the distance another car travels. The total distance traveled by both cars is 350 miles.
12B) The area of one room is 5 more than twice the area of another room. The total area of the rooms is 250 square feet.
Solutions:
12A) Let x be the distance traveled by one car and $3x - 4$ be the distanced traveled by the

other car. So we have
$3x - 4 + x = 350$.
12B) Let x be the area of one room and let $2x + 5$ be the area of the other room. So we have
$2x + 5 + x = 250$.

EXAMPLE 13:
Write the following problems as equations.
13A) Tony Haller is 2 more than half the age of his mother. The sum of Tony's and his mother's ages is 72 years.
13B) Richard Walker is 3 less than 3 times his daughter's age. The difference of their ages is 34 years.
Solutions:
13A) Let x be his mother's age and let $\frac{1}{2}x + 2$ be Tony's age.
Then we have $\frac{1}{2}x + 2 + x = 72$.
13B) Let x be his daughter's age and let $3x - 3$ be Richard's age. Then we have
$3x - 3 - x = 34$.

EXAMPLE 14:
Express each problem as an equation.
14A) Marilyn Monson rented a lawnmower for y days at a cost of $25 per day. The cost of renting the lawnmower was $125.
14B) Jack Payne drove for x days, and averaged 350 miles per day. Jack drove a total of 3500 miles.
14C) Janice Palmer rented a car for p days at a cost of $40 per day. The cost of renting the car was $160.
14D) Ursula Smythe jogged for x days and averaged 5 miles per day. She jogged a total of 60 miles.
14E) The population of a town is decreasing by 100 people per year. The decrease in population in t years is 1200.

14F) Marjorie Albin's salary has increased by $450 per year. The increase in her salary in x years is $2700.
14G) Then number of cents in d dimes is 150.
14H) The number of cents in q quarters is 275.
Solutions:
14A) $25y = 125$
14B) $350x = 3500$
14C) $40p = 160$
14D) $5x = 60$
14E) $100t = 1200$
14F) $450x = 2700$
14G) $10d = 150$
14H) $25q = 275$

Section 3.3
EXAMPLE 1:
1A) Five subtracted from 6 times a number is 7. Find the number.
1B) 16 less than 22 times a number is 94. Find the number.
Solutions:
1A) 2   **1B)** 5

EXAMPLE 2:
2A) The sum of two numbers is 62. Find the two numbers if the larger number is 4 less than twice the smaller number.
2B) The difference between two numbers is 10. Find the numbers if the smaller number is 6 more than half the larger number.
Solutions:
2A) 22 and 40   **2B)** 22 and 32

EXAMPLE 3:
3A) The Gothenburg Greenhouse produces tomatoes year-round. This year 300 plants will be planted. Each year thereafter, 120 more plants will be planted until 1140 plants are planted annually. How long will it take for them to reach this goal?
3B) The population of Winnebago is 2135. If the

population of the town is decreasing by 12 persons per year, how long will it take for the population to decrease to 2000 people?
Solutions:
3A) 7 years
3B) 11 years, 3 months

EXAMPLE 4:
4A) Eldorado Jimenez needs to rent a car. He only has $100 to use for the rental. The cost of renting the car is $50 per day plus $0.40 per mile. Find the maximum distance Eldorado can drive.
4B) Tianna James is moving and needs to rent a moving van for two days. The cost of renting the truck is $65 per day plus $0.45 cents per mile. Find the maximum distance Tianna can drive if she only has $200 to spend for this expense?
Solutions:
4A) 125 miles
4B) 300 miles

EXAMPLE 5:
5A) Brianna Haynes is considering two different companies for her cell phone service. She needs a plan that gives her 300 anytime minutes and free long distance anywhere in the U.S. Allnet's startup fee is $35 plus a monthly fee of $30 for the plan described above. Teleco's startup fee is $10 plus a montly fee of $35 for the plan described above. In how many months would the total cost of Allnet's and Teleco's 300-minute plans be the same?
5B) Henry Jamison is considering two different companies for his cable TV service. NetTV charges a $50 startup fee plus a monthly fee of $20. Coxian charges a $30 startup fee plus a monthly fee of $25. When will the cost of the two services be the same?
Solutions:
5A) 5 months   **5B)** 4 months

EXAMPLE 6:
6A) Martina Ray is considering two different companies for her home mortgage. Bank of New England will require a monthly payment of $720 plus she will need to pay fees of $1000 to obtain the mortgage. New Bank requires a monthly payment of $800. How long will it take for the total cost of both mortgages to be the same?
6B) Reginald Northcut is seeking a home mortgage. Sun Bank will offer a monthly payment of $650 plus a one-time fee of $1250. First Bank will offer a monthly payment of $700 plus a one-time fee of $950. How long will it take for the total cost of both mortgages to be the same?
Solutions:
6A) 12.5 months
6B) 6 months

EXAMPLE 7:
7A) The cost of a meal at Surfside is $17.11, which includes a 7% sales tax. What is the original cost of the meal?
7B) The cost of a DVD player from the Furniture Mart costs $346.13, which includes a 6.5% sales tax. Find the cost of the DVD player before tax.
Solutions:
7A) $15.99   **7B)** $325

EXAMPLE 8:
7A) Gregory Thompson received an 8% increase in his salary from last year. His salary this year is $53,000. What was his salary last year?
7B) Brenda Ayers received a salary increase of 5.5% from last year. If her salary this year is $65,250, what was her salary last year?
Solutions:
7A) $49,074.07
7B) $61,848.34

EXAMPLE 9:
9A) Jaquita Jones has received two job offers from sales companies. The first company offers a $500 base salary plus 4% commission of weekly sales. The second company offers a straight 8% commission of weekly sales. **a)** What must Jaquita's weekly sales be in order for the two offers to be the same? **b)** If Jaquita is certain that she can make $15,000 in sales per week, which offer should she select?
9B) A certain sales company offers two salary plans. Plan A is a $750 base salary plus a 3.5% commission of weekly sales. Plan B is a $350 base salary plus a 7.5% commission of weekly sales. **a)** What should the weekly sales be for the two plans to produce the same salary? **b)** If a salesperson knows they can make $12000 in sales per week, which offer should he take?
Solutions:
9A) a) $12,500; **b)** The offer from the second company
9B) a) $10,000; **b)** Plan B

Section 3.4
EXAMPLE 1:
1A) Cassie McGill will be building a rectangular deck off the back of her house. The length of the deck is to be 10 feet longer than the width. She has 60 feet of railing to surround the deck. Find the dimensions of the patio Cassie plans to build.
1B) The width of a rectangular driveway is to be 7 less than half the length of the driveway. If the perimeter of the driveway is to be 106 feet, find the dimensions of the driveway.
Solutions:
1A) The width of the deck will be 10 feet and the length will be 20 feet.

1B) The width of the driveway will be 13 feet and the length will be 40 feet.

EXAMPLE 2:
2A) The measures of each of the base angles of an isosceles triangle are 12 more than the measure of the other angle of the triangle. Find the measure of each angle.
2B) In a triangle, the measure of the medium-sized angle is 1 more than twice the measure of the smallest angle. The measure of the largest angle is 13 less than 3 times the measure of the smallest angle. Find the measure of the angles.
Solutions:
2A) 52°, 64°, and 64°
2B) 32°, 65°, and 83°

EXAMPLE 3:
3A) In an isosceles trapezoid, the measure of the top two angles are the same and the measure of the bottom two angle is the same. If the measure of the bottom two angles is 30 more than half the measure of the top two angles, find the measure of each angle.
3B) In a quadrilateral, the measure of one angle is twice the measure of the smallest angle. The measure of another angle is 10 more than twice the smallest angle. Finally, the measure of a third angle is 10 less than 3 times the measure of the smallest angle. Find the measure of each angle.
Solutions:
3A) 80°, 80°, 100°, 100°
3B) 45°, 90°, 100°, 125°

EXAMPLE 4:
4A) A bookshelf has a length that is 2 less than twice its width. The shelf will have 3 shelves. What are the dimensions of the bookshelf if the total length of wood used to build the shelf is 41 feet? (See figure below)

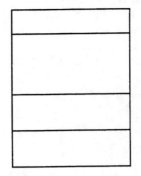

4B) A garden has a width that is 4 more than half its length. There is a sting-fence around the garden. The owner also uses a string-fence to divide the garden into five sections. The total amount of string fence used is 184 feet. Find the dimensions of the garden.

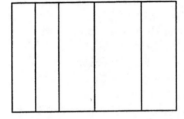

Solutions:
4A) 5 feet by 8 feet
4B) 20 feet by 32 feet

Section 3.5
EXAMPLE 1:
1A) Mike Smithey works for a mail processing center. He can process mail at a rate of 362 pieces per hour. How many pieces can he process per 8-hour workday?
1B) Cassandra Jillian walks at a rate of 0.9 miles per 15 minutes. How many miles can she walk in 1 hour?
Solutions:
1A) 2,896 pieces **1B)** 3.6 miles

EXAMPLE 2:
3A) Evelyn Gregory runs at a rate of 6.2 miles per hour. How long will it take her to run a marathon, which is 26.2 miles?

3B) A certain worm can move at a rate of 16 inches per minute. How long would it take the worm to move 5 feet?
Solutions:
3A) Approximately 4.2 hours
3B) 3.75 minutes

EXAMPLE 3:
3A) Two joggers, Ron and Jill, are 6 miles apart and they are running towards each other. They began running at the same time. Ron is running 0.5 miles per hour faster than Jill. After 20 minutes, Ron and Jill meet each other. How fast are Ron and Jill running?
3B) Two trains depart from the same station at the same time. They are traveling in opposite directions. After 45 minutes, the trains are 82.5 miles apart. One train is traveling at a rate of 10 mph faster than the other train. How fast is each train traveling?
Solutions:
3A) Jill's rate is 8.75 mph, while Ron's rate is 8.25mph.
3B) 50 mph and 60 mph

EXAMPLE 4:
4A) Two construction crews are 30 miles apart working towards each other. Both are laying pipe in a straight line that will eventually be connected together. Both crews work the same amount of time. Once crew works at a rate that is 0.25 mile per day slower than the other crew. If they complete the job in 8 days, find the rate of each crew.
4B) Two boats leave from the same dock, one traveling due west and the other due east. After 2 hours, the boats are 150 miles apart. The boat heading due west is traveling 5 mph faster than the other boat. Find the speeds of the boats.
Solutions:
4A) 1.75 and 2 miles per day
4B) 35 and 40 mph

EXAMPLE 5:

5A) Zoe and Bill are scheduled to go on a morning bike ride at 6:00 A.M. On the day of the ride, Zoe shows up at their meeting point at 5:55 A.M. She waits for Bill until 6:15, and decides to ride without Bill when he doesn't show. At 6:30, Bill arrives at the meeting place, and continues to ride in the same direction as Zoe in an attempt to catch her. Zoe is riding at a rate of 10 mph. Bill rides at a rate of 15 mph. **a)** How long will it take Bill to catch up to Zoe? **b)** How far from their starting point will they be when they meet?

5B) A person has stolen a car and takes off down the interstate. He stops at a rest area and leaves again at 11:00 P.M. Based on a tip, a policeman arrives at the rest area at 11:05. She sees that the stolen car is no longer at the rest area, and takes after the thief down the interstate. The thief is traveling at a speed of 80 mph and the policeman travels at a speed of 100 mph. **a)** How long does it take the policeman to catch up to the thief? **b)** How far from the rest area will the policeman and thief be when they meet?

Solutions:

5A) a) 30 minutes; **b)** 7.5 miles

5B) a) 20 minutes; **b)** Approximately 33.3 miles

EXAMPLE 6:

6A) Abigail Adams has invested $20,000, part in an investment that pays 4% annual interest, and part in an investment that pays 6% annual interest. If Abigail earned $960 in interest after 1 year, how did she invest in each investment?

6B) Herbert Haver invested $10,000 one year ago. He used two investments, one that earned $4 \frac{1}{8}$ % and one that earned $5 \frac{3}{4}$ %. If he earned a total of

$485.62 after one year, how much did he invest in each investment?

Solutions:

6A) $16,000 at 4% and $4000 at 6%

6B) $5,500 at $4 \frac{1}{8}$ % and $4,500 at $5 \frac{3}{4}$ % (rounded to the nearest dollar)

EXAMPLE 7:

7A) Janice Vosler sells two types of fruit baskets. The larger basket costs $36 and the smaller basket costs $20. She sold a total of 62 baskets over the Holiday season and received $1832 in payment for the baskets. How many of each type of basket did she sell?

7B) The Harmony Group, a local charity organization, recently held a concert to raise money for their cause. Adult tickets were $15 and student tickets were $8. There were 361 people in attendance at the event. The total received for the cost of tickets was $4,841. How many adult and children tickets were sold?

Solutions:

7A) 37 large baskets and 25 small baskets

7B) 279 adult tickets and 82 children tickets

EXAMPLE 8:

8A) Kelly Gatewood, a chemistry instructor, needs a 15% hydrochloric acid solution for an experiment. After searching through the chemistry storage room, she finds only 10% and 25% hydrochloric acid solutions available. How many liters of the 10% solution must she add to 6 liters of the 25% solution to get a solution that is 15% hydrochloric acid?

8B) Joe Marik owns a fish aquarium. The fish must be kept in salt water with a 0.75% salt content. During a particularly

dry month, some of the tanks water evaporates and the salt content increases to 0.8%. How much pure water must Joe add to the 10 gallons in the tank to lower the salt concentration to 0.75%.

Solutions:

8A) 12 liters   **8B)** $\frac{2}{3}$ gallon

EXAMPLE 9:

9A) A candy store at the Westville shopping center sells a candy mixture for $3.75 per pound. The candy mixture contains assorted chocolate mini candy bars, which sell for $2.75 per pound. The mixture also contains licorice drops that sell for $4.50 per pound. If the store owner wants to use 5 pounds of the licorice candy to make the mixture, how many pounds of the chocolate mini candy bars must be added to make the mixture?

9B) At the Coffee Bean, a customer favorite has become a mixture of Irish Crème and Morning Roast flavored coffees. The Irish Crème coffee sells for $5.50 per pound and the Morning Roast coffee sells for $3.75 per pound. The store-owner sells the mixture for $4.45 per pound. One container of the mixture was made with 10 pounds of the Irish Crème coffee. How much of the Morning Roast coffee was added to the 10 pounds of Irish Crème to make the mixture that costs $4.45 per pound?

Solutions:

9A) 3.75 pounds **9B)** 15 pounds

Chapter 4: Exponents and Polynomials

Section 4.1

EXAMPLE 1:
Write each expression using exponents.
1A) $aabbbbbbb$
1B) $xxxxyyyyzz$
Solutions:
1A) a^2b^7 **1B)** $x^4y^5z^2$

EXAMPLE 2:
Multiply.
2A) $a^3 \bullet a^5$ **2B)** $x^4 \bullet x^{10}$
Solutions:
2A) a^8 **2B)** x^{14}

EXAMPLE 3:
Multiply each expression using the product rule.
3A) $4^3 \bullet 4$ **3B)** $3^3 \bullet 3^2$
3C) $y \bullet y^2$ **3D)** $y^5 \bullet y^2$
3E) $x^{10} \bullet x^3$
Solutions:
3A) 4^4 **3B)** 3^5
3C) y^3 **3D)** y^7
3E) x^{13}

EXAMPLE 4:
Divide.
4A) $a^6 \div a^4$ **4B)** $x^7 \div x$
Solutions:
4A) a^2 **4B)** x^6

EXAMPLE 5:
Divide each expression using the quotient rule.
5A) $\dfrac{4^6}{4^3}$ **5B)** $\dfrac{3^5}{3}$
5C) $\dfrac{y^8}{y^2}$ **5D)** $\dfrac{y^{14}}{y^6}$
5E) $\dfrac{x^9}{x}$

Solutions:
5A) 4^4 **5B)** 3^4
5C) y^6 **5D)** y^8
5E) x^8

EXAMPLE 6:
Simplify by dividing out a common factor in both the numerator and denominator.
6A) $\dfrac{x^8}{x^{12}}$ **6B)** $\dfrac{y^6}{y^8}$
Solutions:
6A) $\dfrac{1}{x^4}$ **6B)** $\dfrac{1}{y^2}$

EXAMPLE 7:
Divide.
7A) $\dfrac{a^5}{a^5}$ **7B)** $\dfrac{x^9}{x^9}$
Solutions:
7A) 1   **7B)** 1

EXAMPLE 8:
Simplify each expression.
Assume $y \neq 0$.
8A) 4^0 **8B)** y^0
8C) $4y^0$ **8D)** $10x^0$
8E) $(4y)^0$ **8F)** $(6b)^0$
8G) $5x^2y^5z^0$ **8H)** $-ab^0c^7$
Solutions:
8A) 1   **8B)** 1
8C) 4   **8D)** 10
8E) 1   **8F)** 1
8G) $5x^2y^5$ **8H)** $-ac^7$

EXAMPLE 9:
Simplify.
9A) $(a^4)^2$ **9B)** $\left(x^6\right)^3$
Solutions:
9A) a^8 **9B)** x^{18}

EXAMPLE 10:
Simplify.
10A) $(x^4)^3$ **10B)** $(2^2)^3$
10C) $(b^6)^5$ **10D)** $\left(y^3\right)^{33}$

Solutions:
10A) x^{12} **10B)** 2^6 or 64
10C) b^{30} **10D)** y^{99}

EXAMPLE 11:
Simplify.
11A) $\left(\dfrac{bx}{ay}\right)^3$ **11B)** $\left(\dfrac{mn}{pq}\right)^4$
Solutions:
11A) $\dfrac{b^3x^3}{a^3y^3}$ **11B)** $\dfrac{m^4n^4}{p^4q^4}$

EXAMPLE 12:
Simplify each expression.
12A) $(3b)^3$ **12B)** $(2x)^5$
12C) $(-y)^5$ **12D)** $(-x)^7$
12E) $(2ab)^4$ **12F)** $(3xy)^3$
12G) $\left(\dfrac{-2y}{3x}\right)^2$ **12H)** $\left(\dfrac{3a}{-4b}\right)^2$
Solutions:
12A) $27b^3$ **12B)** $32x^5$
12C) $-y^5$ **12D)** $-x^7$
12E) $16a^4b^4$ **12F)** $27x^3y^3$
12G) $\dfrac{4y^2}{9x^2}$ **12H)** $\dfrac{9a^2}{16b^2}$

EXAMPLE 13:
Simplify.
13A) $\left(\dfrac{8x^5y^2}{4x^2y}\right)^4$ **13B)** $\left(\dfrac{10x^3y^6}{5x^2y^8}\right)^3$
Solutions:
13A) $16x^{12}y^4$ **13B)** $\dfrac{8x^3}{y^6}$

EXAMPLE 14:
Simplify.
14A) $\left(\dfrac{18x^2y^8}{6x^5y^4}\right)^3$ **14B)** $\left(\dfrac{15a^3b^4}{5a^2b^5}\right)^4$
Solutions:
14A) $\dfrac{27y^{12}}{x^9}$ **14B)** $\dfrac{81a^4}{b^4}$

EXAMPLE 15:
Simplify.

15A) $(3x^3y^2)^3(x^2y)$

15B) $(4b^2c^4)^2(bc^2)$

Solutions:

15A) $27x^{11}y^7$ **15B)** $16b^5c^{10}$

Section 4.2

EXAMPLE 1:

1A) Simplify x^2/x^5 by **a)** using the quotient rule and **b)** dividing out common factors.

1B) Simplify y^8/y^{15} by **a)** using the quotient rule and **b)** dividing out common factors.

Solutions:

1A) $\dfrac{1}{x^3}$ **1B)** $\dfrac{1}{y^7}$

EXAMPLE 2:
Use the negative exponent rule to write each expression with a positive exponent.

2A) x^{-4} **2B)** y^{-2}

2C) 2^{-3} **2D)** 4^{-1}

2E) -3^{-2} **2F)** -5^{-3}

2G) $(-3)^{-4}$ **2H)** $(-5)^{-3}$

Solutions:

2A) $\dfrac{1}{x^4}$ **2B)** $\dfrac{1}{y^2}$

2C) $\dfrac{1}{8}$ **2D)** $\dfrac{1}{4}$

2E) $-\dfrac{1}{9}$ **2F)** $-\dfrac{1}{125}$

2G) $\dfrac{1}{81}$ **2H)** $-\dfrac{1}{125}$

EXAMPLE 3:
Use the negative exponent rule to write each expression with a positive exponent.

3A) $\dfrac{1}{x^{-5}}$ **3B)** $\dfrac{1}{y^{-7}}$

3C) $\dfrac{1}{3^{-1}}$ **3D)** $\dfrac{1}{2^{-4}}$

Solutions:

3A) x^5 **3B)** y^7

3B) 3 **3C)** 16

EXAMPLE 4:
Simplify.

4A) $(x^{-2})^7$ **4B)** $(c^{-10})^2$

4C) $(3^3)^{-2}$ **4D)** $(4^9)^{-3}$

Solutions:

4A) $\dfrac{1}{x^{14}}$ **4B)** $\dfrac{1}{c^{20}}$

4C) $\dfrac{1}{3^6}$ **4D)** $\dfrac{1}{4^{27}}$

EXAMPLE 5:
Simplify.

5A) $x^4 \bullet x^{-7}$ **5B)** $x^{-16} \bullet x^{10}$

5C) $2^{-3} \bullet 2^{-9}$ **5D)** $3^{-2} \bullet 3^{-5}$

Solutions:

5A) $\dfrac{1}{x^3}$ **5B)** $\dfrac{1}{x^6}$

5C) $\dfrac{1}{2^{12}}$ **5D)** $\dfrac{1}{3^7}$

EXAMPLE 6:
Simplify.

6A) $\dfrac{x^{-3}}{x^9}$ **6B)** $\dfrac{b^{-2}}{b^{12}}$

6C) $\dfrac{5^{-8}}{5^{-3}}$ **6D)** $\dfrac{2^{-6}}{2^{-3}}$

Solutions:

6A) $\dfrac{1}{x^{12}}$ **6B)** $\dfrac{1}{b^{14}}$

6C) $\dfrac{1}{5^5}$ **6D)** $\dfrac{1}{2^3}$

EXAMPLE 7:
Simplify.

7A) $3y^3(4y^{-4})$ **7B)** $(3b^{-3})4a^4$

7C) $\dfrac{10x^4y^{-4}}{5xy^3}$ **7D)** $\dfrac{12a^{-2}b^4}{3ab^2}$

7E) $\dfrac{3x^3y^6}{12x^8y^{-4}}$ **7F)** $\dfrac{5a^4b^7}{15a^{-5}b^6}$

Solutions:

7A) $\dfrac{12}{y}$ **7B)** $\dfrac{12a^4}{b^3}$

7C) $\dfrac{2x^3}{y^7}$ **7D)** $\dfrac{4b^2}{a^3}$

7E) $\dfrac{y^{10}}{4x^5}$ **7F)** $\dfrac{a^9b}{3}$

EXAMPLE 8:
Simplify.

8A) $(4y^{-5})^{-2}$ **8B)** $(2b^{-3})^{-3}$

Solutions:

8A) $\dfrac{y^{10}}{16}$ **8B)** $\dfrac{b^9}{8}$

EXAMPLE 9:
Simplify.

9A) $\left(\dfrac{4}{9}\right)^{-2}$ **9B)** $\left(\dfrac{2}{3}\right)^{-3}$

Solutions:

9A) $\dfrac{81}{16}$ **9B)** $\dfrac{27}{8}$

EXAMPLE 10:
Simplify.

10A) $\left(\dfrac{4}{3}\right)^{-2}$ **10B)** $\left(\dfrac{3}{4}\right)^{-4}$

10C) $\left(\dfrac{a}{b}\right)^{-3}$ **10D)** $\left(\dfrac{x}{y}\right)^{-6}$

Solutions:

10A) $\dfrac{9}{16}$ **10B)** $\dfrac{256}{81}$

10C) $\dfrac{b^3}{a^3}$ **10D)** $\dfrac{y^6}{x^6}$

EXAMPLE 11:
Simplify.

11A) $\left(\dfrac{x^3y^{-2}}{z^3}\right)^{-6}$

11B) $\left(\dfrac{a^{-3}b^{-4}}{c^5}\right)^{-3}$

11C) $\left(\dfrac{2x^{-2}y^3z^2}{x^5}\right)^3$

11D) $\left(\dfrac{3a^{-3}b^4c^6}{b^{-3}} \right)^2$

Solutions:

11A) $\dfrac{y^{12}z^{18}}{x^{18}}$ **11B)** $a^9b^{12}c^{15}$

11C) $\dfrac{8y^9z^6}{x^{21}}$ **11D)** $\dfrac{9b^{14}c^{12}}{a^6}$

Section 4.3

EXAMPLE 1:
Write the following numbers in scientific notation.
1A) 11,890   **1B)** 0.0000786
1C) 1,860,000   **1D)** 0.0023
Solutions:
1A) 1.189×10^4 **1B)** 7.86×10^{-5}
1C) 1.86×10^6 **1D)** 2.3×10^{-3}

EXAMPLE 2:
Write each number without exponents.
2A) 4.6×10^6 **2B)** 5.23×10^{-2}
2C) 2.89×10^9 **2D)** 7.003×10^{-9}
Solutions:
2A) 4,600,000   **2B)** 0.0523
2C) 2,890,000,000
2D) 0.000000007003

EXAMPLE 3:
Multiply.
3A) $(2.8 \times 10^7)(3 \times 10^{-3})$
3B) $(3.25 \times 10^{-5})(4.001 \times 10^9)$
Solutions:
3A) 8.4×10^4 **3B)** 1.300325×10^5

EXAMPLE 4:
Divide.
4A) $\dfrac{4.2 \times 10^{-6}}{2 \times 10^{-4}}$ **4B)** $\dfrac{5.6 \times 10^{-3}}{28 \times 10^{-7}}$
Solutions:
4A) 2.1×10^{-2} **4B)** 2.0×10^3

EXAMPLE 5:
5A) The weight of the Earth is 5.972×10^{24} kg. The weight of the Earth's moon is 7.35×10^{22} kg. **a)** How much greater is the weight of the Earth than the weight of it's moon? **b)** How many times greater is the weight of the Earth than the weight of it's moon.
5B) At the end of 2002, the U.S. national debt was approximately $6.421 x 10^{12}. The population of the U.S. at the end of 2002 was approximately 2.88×10^8 persons. What is each U.S. citizen's share of the national debt?
Solutions:
5A) a) 5.8985×10^{24}; **b)** Approximately 81 times greater
5B) $22,295.14

EXAMPLE 6:
6A) A computer can perform a single operations in 0.00000045 second. How long would it take this computer to do 8 trillion operations?
6B) Suppose 6 trillion molecules of a certain substance can fit into 1000 square inches. In what amount of space will one of these molecules fit?
Solutions:
6A) 3,600,000 seconds
6B) Approximately 1.67×10^{-10} square inches

Section 4.4

EXAMPLE 1:
Simplify.
1A) $(3x^2 + 5x + 5) + (3x^2 + 3x - 2)$
1B) $(6x^2 + 7x - 6) + (2x^2 + 9x - 2)$
Solutions:
1A) $6x^2 + 8x + 3$
1B) $8x^2 + 16x - 8$

EXAMPLE 2:
Simplify.
1A) $(5x^2 + 2x + y) + (x^2 - 4x + 5)$
1B) $(7a^2 + a + b) + (10a^2 - 3a + 9)$
Solutions:
1A) $6x^2 - 2x + y + 5$
1B) $17a^2 - 2a + b + 9$

EXAMPLE 3:
Simplify.
3A) $(3x^2y - 5xy + y) + (x^2y + 4xy + 8y)$
3B) $(5a^2b + ab + 2b) + (7a^2b - 3ab - b)$
Solutions:
3A) $4x^2y - xy + 9y$
3B) $12a^2b - 2ab + b$

EXAMPLE 4:
Add using columns.
4A) $6x^2 - 3x + 3$ and $-3x^2 - x + 5$
4B) $2a^2 + 9a - 10$ and $-6a^2 + 4a + 4$
Solutions:
4A) $3x^2 - 4x + 8$
4B) $-4a^2 + 13a - 6$

EXAMPLE 5:
Add using columns.
5A) $(4x^3 + 3x - 4)$ and $(4x^2 - 5x - 7)$
5B) $(6m^3 + 4m + 9)$ and $(6m^2 + 3m - 8)$
Solutions:
5A) $4x^3 + 4x^2 - 2x - 11$
5B) $6m^3 + 6m^2 + 7m + 1$

EXAMPLE 6:
Simplify.
6A) $(4x^2 - 3x + 6) - (x^2 - 7x + 8)$
6B) $(a^2 + 3a + 1) - (9a^2 - 7a - 10)$
Solutions:
6A) $3x^2 + 4x - 2$
6B) $-8a^2 + 10a + 11$

EXAMPLE 7:
7A) Subtract $(-x^2 - 4x + 2)$ from $(x^3 + 3x + 9)$.
7B) Subtract $-2a^2 + 5a - 2$ from $7a^4 + 2a + 6$.
Solutions:
7A) $x^3 + x^2 + 7x + 7$
7B) $7a^4 + 2a^2 - 3a + 8$

EXAMPLE 8:
8A) Subtract $(x^2 - 5x + 4)$ from $(4x^2 + 7x + 6)$ using columns.

8B) Subtract $2a^2 + 3a - 9$ from $5a^2 - 13a + 19$ using columns.
Solutions:
8A) $3x^2 + 12x + 2$
8B) $3a^2 - 16a + 26$

EXAMPLE 9:
9A) Subtract $(3x^2 - 8)$ from $(-4x^3 + 7x - 5)$ using columns.
9B) Subtract $5a^3 - 5a + 4$ from $9a^4 + 8a$ using columns.
Solutions:
9A) $-4x^3 - 3x^2 + 7x + 3$
9B) $9a^4 - 5a^3 + 13a - 4$

Section 4.5
EXAMPLE 1:
Multiply.
1A) $(3x^3)(4x^4)$ **1B)** $(5a^6)(3a^2)$
1C) $(-x^8)(4x^3)$ **1D)** $(9a^3)(-5a^4)$
Solutions:
1A) $12x^7$ **1B)** $15a^8$
1C) $-4x^{11}$ **1D)** $-45a^7$

EXAMPLE 2:
Multiply.
2A) $(5x^3 y)(6x^3 y^7)$
2B) $(7a^4 b)(8a^2 b^6)$
Solutions:
2A) $30x^6 y^8$ **2B)** $56a^6 b^7$

EXAMPLE 3:
Multiply.
3A) $(-9xy^2 z^6)(3x^4 yz^9)$
3B) $(-a^4 bc^4)(-9a^2 bc^3)$
3C) $(12y^4 z)(-3x^4 yz^9)$
3D) $(-8a^6 bc^2)(2a^2 c^3)$
Solutions:
3A) $-27x^5 y^3 z^{15}$ **3B)** $9a^6 b^2 c^7$
3C) $-36x^4 y^5 z^{10}$ **3D)** $-16a^8 bc^5$

EXAMPLE 4:
Multiply.
4A) $4x(x^2 + 5)$ **4B)** $6a(a^2 + 10)$
Solutions:
4A) $4x^3 + 20x$ **4B)** $6a^3 + 60a$

EXAMPLE 5:
Multiply.
5A) $-2x(2x^2 - 3x - 5)$
5B) $6a(a^2 + 5a - 7)$
Solutions:
5A) $-4x^3 + 6x^2 + 10x$
5B) $6a^3 + 30a^2 - 42a$

EXAMPLE 6:
Multiply.
6A) $3x^2(5x^3 - 3x + 8)$
6B) $3a^3(2a^2 + 2a - 7)$
Solutions:
6A) $15x^5 - 9x^3 + 24x^2$
6B) $6a^5 + 6a^4 - 21a^3$

EXAMPLE 7:
Multiply.
7A) $2x(4x^2 y - 7xy + 2)$
7B) $2b(5b^2 c + 8bc - 1)$
Solutions:
7A) $8x^3 y - 14x^2 y + 4x$
7B) $10b^3 c + 16b^2 c - 2b$

EXAMPLE 8:
Multiply.
8A) $(5x^2 - 3xy + 5)3x$
8B) $(2a^2 - 6ab - 3)2b$
Solutions:
8A) $15x^3 - 9x^2 y + 15x$
8B) $4a^2 b - 12ab^2 - 6b$

EXAMPLE 9:
Multiply.
9A) $(2x + 3)(x - 3)$
9B) $(5a + 3)(a - 2)$
Solutions:
9A) $2x^2 - 3x - 9$
9B) $5a^2 - 7a - 6$

EXAMPLE 10:
Multiply.
10A) $(x - 3)(y + 5)$
10B) $(a + 3)(b - 9)$
Solutions:
10A) $xy + 5x - 3y - 15$
10B) $ab - 9a + 3b - 27$

EXAMPLE 11:
Using the FOIL method, multiply.
11A) $(3x - 2)(x + 2)$
11B) $(8a + 3)(2a - 5)$
Solutions:
11A) $3x^2 + 4x - 4$
11B) $16a^2 - 34a - 15$

EXAMPLE 12:
Multiply.
12A) $(2 - 5x)(7 - 2x)$
12B) $(8 - 3b)(7 - 5b)$
Solutions:
12A) $14 - 39x + 10x^2$ or $10x^2 - 39x + 14$
12B) $56 - 61b + 15b^2$ or $15b^2 - 61b + 56$

EXAMPLE 13:
Multiply.
13A) $(3x - 5)(3x + 5)$
13B) $(5c + 4)(5c - 4)$
Solutions:
13A) $9x^2 - 25$ **13B)** $25c^2 - 16$

EXAMPLE 14:
Use the rule for finding the product of the sum and difference of two quantities to multiply each expression.
14A) $(x + 10)(x - 10)$
14B) $(b - 7)(b + 7)$
14C) $(6x - 2)(6x + 2)$
14D) $(3a + 12)(3a - 12)$
14E) $(2x + 5y)(2x - 5y)$
14F) $(7a - 2b)(7a + 2b)$
Solutions:
14A) $x^2 - 100$ **14B)** $b^2 - 49$
14C) $36x^2 - 4$ **14D)** $9a^2 - 144$
14E) $4x^2 - 25$ **14F)** $49a^2 - 4b^2$

EXAMPLE 15:
Using the FOIL method, find:
15A) $(x + 8)^2$ **15B)** $(a - 4)^2$
Solutions:
15A) $x^2 + 16x + 64$
15B) $a^2 - 8a + 16$

EXAMPLE 16:
Use the square of a binomial formula to multiply each expression.

16A) $(x+12)^2$ **16B)** $(a+13)^2$

16C) $(x-4)^2$ **16D)** $(b-2)^2$

16E) $(3x+5)^2$ **16F)** $(2b+4)^2$

16G) $(2x-3y)^2$ **16H)** $(7r-w)^2$

Solutions:

16A) $x^2+24x+144$

16B) $a^2+26a+169$

16C) $x^2-8x+16$

16D) b^2-4b+4

16E) $9x^2+30x+25$

16F) $4b^2+16b+16$

16G) $4x^2-12xy+9y^2$

16H) $49r^2-14rw+w^2$

EXAMPLE 17:
Multiply.

17A) $(4x+2)(3x+9)$

17B) $(3a+7)(4a+6)$

Solutions:

17A) $12x^2+42x+18$

17B) $12a^2+46a+42$

EXAMPLE 18:
Multiply.

18A) $(2x-3)(3x^2+4x-2)$

18B) $(3a+2)(4a^2-a+3)$

Solutions:

18A) $6x^3-x^2-16x+6$

18B) $12a^3+5a^2+7a+6$

EXAMPLE 19:
Multiply.

19A) x^2-4x+3 by $(3x^2-4)$.

19B) $2x^2-8x-4$ by (x^2+6)

Solutions:

19A) $3x^4-12x^3+5x^2+16x-12$

19B) $2x^4-8x^3+8x^2-48x-24$

EXAMPLE 20:
Multiply.

20A) $(2x^3-3x^2+5x+3)(x^2-4x)$

20B) $(4a^3+2a^2-a+4)(2a^2+2a)$

Solutions:

20A) $2x^5-11x^4+17x^3-17x^2-12x$

20B) $8a^5+12a^4+2a^3+6a^2+8a$

Section 4.6

EXAMPLE 1:
Divide.

1A) $\dfrac{3x+18}{3}$

1B) $\dfrac{6x+20}{2}$

1C) $\dfrac{39x^2-12x}{3x}$

1D) $\dfrac{48x^2-16x}{4x}$

Solutions:

1A) $x+6$ **1B)** $3x+10$

1C) $13x-4$ **1D)** $16x-4$

EXAMPLE 2:
Divide.

2A) $\dfrac{6x^5-4x^4+12x-5}{2x^2}$

2B) $\dfrac{8x^6+12x^4-6x^3-3}{3x^2}$

Solutions:

2A) $3x^3-2x^2+\dfrac{6}{x}-\dfrac{5}{2x^2}$

2B) $\dfrac{8x^4}{3}+4x^2-2x-\dfrac{1}{x^2}$

EXAMPLE 3:
Divide.

3A) $\dfrac{8x^3-2x^2+6x-1}{-2x}$

3B) $\dfrac{7x^3+9x^2-6x+2}{-3x}$

Solutions:

3A) $-4x^2+x-3+\dfrac{1}{2x}$

3B) $-\dfrac{7x^2}{3}-3x+2-\dfrac{2}{3x}$

EXAMPLE 4:
Divide.

4A) $\dfrac{x^2+4x-21}{x-3}$

4B) $\dfrac{x^2-8x+15}{x-5}$

Solutions:

4A) $x+7$ **4B)** $x-3$

EXAMPLE 5:
Divide.

5A) $\dfrac{4x^2-2x+7}{2x+5}$

5B) $\dfrac{6x^2+3x-9}{3x+6}$

Solutions:

5A) $2x-6+\dfrac{37}{2x+5}$

5B) $2x-3+\dfrac{3}{x+2}$

EXAMPLE 6:

6A) Divide $(-18x^2+8x^3-16x-4)$ by $(4x-1)$.

6B) Divide (x^3-1) by $(x-1)$.

Solutions:

6A) $2x^2-4x-5-\dfrac{9}{4x-1}$

6B) x^2+x+1

Chapter 5: Factoring

Section 5.1

EXAMPLE 1:

1A) List the factors of $10y^3$.

1B) List the factors of $4x^2$.

Solutions:

1A) $1, 2, 5, 10, y, 2y, 5y, 10y, y^2,$
$y^3, 5y^2, 10y^2, y^3, 2y^3, 5y^3, 10y^3,$
and the opposites of these factors.

1B) $1, 2, 4, x, 2x, 4x, x^2, 2x^2, 4x^2$
and the opposites of these factors.

EXAMPLE 2:

2A) Write 36 as a product of primes.

2B) Write 128 as a product of primes.

Solutions:

2A) $36 = 2 \bullet 2 \bullet 3 \bullet 3$

2B) $128 = 2 \bullet 2 \bullet 2 \bullet 2 \bullet 2 \bullet 2 \bullet 2$

EXAMPLE 3:

3A) Write 80 as a product of its prime factors.

3B) Write 124 as a product of its prime factors.

Solutions:

3A) $80 = 2 \bullet 2 \bullet 2 \bullet 2 \bullet 5$

3B) $124 = 2 \bullet 2 \bullet 31$

EXAMPLE 4:

4A) Determine the greatest common factor of 36 and 80.

4B) Determine the greatest common factor of 56 and 124.

Solutions:

4A) 4   **4B)** 4

EXAMPLE 5:

5A) Determine the GCF of 48 and 84.

5B) Determine the GCF of 48 and 80.

Solutions:

5A) 12   **5B)** 16

EXAMPLE 6:

6A) Determine the GCF of the terms $m^9, m^3, m^4,$ and m^7.

6B) Determine the GCF of the terms $4x^2, 2x^3, x^5,$ and $8x^7$.

Solutions:

6A) m^3 **6B)** x^2

EXAMPLE 7:

7A) Determine the GCF of the terms $a^2b^7, a^4b,$ and a^8b^2.

7B) Determine the GCF of the terms $4x^2y, 2x^3y^3, 2xy^2,$
and $8x^7y$.

Solutions:

7A) a^2b **7B)** $2xy$

EXAMPLE 8:

8A) Determine the GCF of the terms $ab, a^3b,$ and b^2.

8B) Determine the GCF of the terms $w^4x^2, w^2x^3,$ and w^5x^3.

Solutions:

8A) b **8B)** w^2x^2

EXAMPLE 9:

Determine the GCF of each set of terms.

9A) $12b^3, 18ab^2, 28a^4b$

9B) $18x^2y^3, -24xy^4, 32x^4y^2$

9C) $y^3, 9y^3, y^2$

Solutions:

9A) $2b$ **9B)** $2xy^2$

9C) y^2

EXAMPLE 10:

Determine the GCF of each pair of terms.

10A) $y(y-2)$ and $3(y-2)$

10B) $3(x+6)$ and $x+6$

10C) $3a(a-b)$ and $5(a-b)$

Solutions:

10A) $(y-2)$ **10B)** $(x+6)$

10C) $(a-b)$

EXAMPLE 11:

11A) Factor $8y+12$.

11B) Factor $12x + 30$

Solutions:

11A) $4(2y+3)$ **11B)** $6(2x+5)$

EXAMPLE 12:

12A) Factor $14x - 28$.

12B) Factor $16w - 48$.

Solutions:

12A) $14(x-2)$

12B) $16(w-3)$

EXAMPLE 13:

13A) Factor $8x^2 + 12x^6$.

13B) Factor $9y^2 + 18y^8$

Solutions:

13A) $4x^2(2+3x^4)$

13B) $9y^2(1+2y^6)$

EXAMPLE 14:

Factor.

14A) $6x^4 + 8x^2 - 18x$

14B) $8x^5 + 12x^2 - 44x$

Solutions:

14A) $2x(3x^3 + 4x - 9)$

14B) $4x(2x^4 + 3x - 11)$

EXAMPLE 15:

Factor.

15A) $44y^2 + 28y - 4$

15B) $60p^2 - 12p - 18$

Solutions:

15A) $4(11y^2 + 7y - 1)$

15B) $6(10p^2 - 2p - 3)$

EXAMPLE 16:

Factor.

16A) $3x^3 + x^2 + 9x^2y$

16B) $5y^4 - 2y^3 + 3xy^3$

Solutions:

16A) $x^2(3x + 1 + 9y)$

16B) $y^3(5y - 2 + 3x)$

EXAMPLE 17:

Factor.

17A) $y(4y-1) + 8(4y-1)$

17B) $x(6r+5) + 9(6r+5)$

Solutions:

17A) $(4y-1)(y+8)$

17B) $(6r+5)(x+9)$

EXAMPLE 18:
Factor.
18A) $4(2y+1)-3y(2y+1)$
18B) $3(3r-7)-2r(3r-7)$
Solutions:
18A) $(4-3y)(2y+1)$
18B) $(3-2r)(3r-7)$

EXAMPLE 19:
Factor.
19A) $3x(x-3)-2(x-3)$
19B) $7x(x-1)-5(x-1)$
Solutions:
19A) $(3x-2)(x-3)$
19B) $(7x-5)(x-1)$

Section 5.2
EXAMPLE 1:
Factor.
1A) $cm+cn+dm+dn$
1B) $fg+hg+fe+he$
Solutions:
1A) $(c+d)(m+n)$
1B) $(g+e)(f+g)$

EXAMPLE 2:
Factor by grouping.
2A) $x^2+2x+6x+12$
2B) $x^2+3x+10x+30$
Solutions:
2A) $(x+6)(x+2)$
2B) $(x+3)(x+10)$

EXAMPLE 3:
Factor by grouping.
3A) $9x^2+6x+15x+10$
3B) $28x^2+8x+21x+6$
Solutions:
3A) $(3x+5)(3x+2)$
3B) $(4x+3)(7x+2)$

EXAMPLE 4:
Factor by grouping.
4A) $30x^2+18x+35x+21$
4B) $8x^2+10x+12x+15$
Solutions:
4A) $(6x+7)(5x+3)$
4B) $(2x+3)(4x+5)$

EXAMPLE 5:
Factor by grouping.
5A) $x^2+7x+x+7$
5B) $x^2+3x+x+3$
Solutions:
5A) $(x+7)(x+1)$
5B) $(x+1)(x+3)$

EXAMPLE 6:
Factor by grouping.
6A) $12x^2-4x-3x+1$
6B) $15x^2-3x-5x+1$
Solutions:
6A) $(4x-1)(3x-1)$
6B) $(3x-1)(5x-1)$

EXAMPLE 7:
Factor by grouping.
7A) $x^2-x+4x-4$
7B) $x^2+5x-x-5$
Solutions:
7A) $(x+4)(x-1)$
7B) $(x+5)(x-1)$

EXAMPLE 8:
Factor by grouping.
8A) $4x^2-8x-3x+6$
8B) $5x^2-15x-2x+6$
Solutions:
8A) $(4x-3)(x-2)$
8B) $(5x-2)(x-3)$

EXAMPLE 9:
Factor by grouping.
9A) $xy+2x-3y-6$
9B) $rt+3t-5r-15$
Solutions:
9A) $(y+2)(x-3)$
9B) $(r+3)(t-5)$

EXAMPLE 10:
Factor.
10A) $6x^2+3xy+4xy+2y^2$
10B) $5x^2+35xy+3xy+21y^2$
Solutions:
10A) $(3x+2y)(2x+y)$
10A) $(5x+3y)(x+7y)$

EXAMPLE 11:
Factor.
11A) $8r^2-12rs+6rs-9s^2$
11B) $21x^2-35xy+6xy-10y^2$
Solutions:
11A) $(4r+3s)(2r-3s)$
11B) $(7x+2y)(3x-5y)$

EXAMPLE 12:
Factor.
12A) $5x^2-10x+15x-30$
12B) $6x^2+30x-18x-90$
Solutions:
12A) $5(x-2)(x+3)$
12B) $6(x-3)(x+5)$

Section 5.3
EXAMPLE 1:
Factor by trial and error.
1A) $x^2+10x+24$
1B) $x^2+12x+20$
Solutions:
1A) $(x+4)(x+6)$
1B) $(x+10)(x+2)$

EXAMPLE 2:
Consider a trinomial of the form x^2+ax+b. Use the signs of a and b given below to determine the signs of the numbers in the factors.
2A) a is positive and b is positive.
2B) a is positive and b is negative.
2C) a is negative and b is negative.
2D) a is negative and b is positive.
Solutions:
2A) Both factors will contain positive numbers.
2B) One factor will contain a negative number, and one will contain a positive number.
2C) One factor will contain a positive number, and one will contain a negative number.
2D) Both factors will contain negative numbers.

EXAMPLE 3:
Factor.
3A) $x^2 + x - 42$
3B) $x^2 + x - 72$
Solutions:
3A) $(x+7)(x-6)$
3B) $(x+9)(x-8)$

EXAMPLE 4:
Factor.
4A) $x^2 - x - 42$
4B) $x^2 - x - 72$
Solutions:
4A) $(x+6)(x-7)$
4B) $(x-9)(x+8)$

EXAMPLE 5:
Factor.
5A) $x^2 - 11x + 30$
5B) $x^2 - 15x + 56$
Solutions:
5A) $(x-5)(x-6)$
5B) $(x-8)(x-7)$

EXAMPLE 6:
Factor.
6A) $x^2 + 4x - 45$
6B) $x^2 + 4x - 32$
Solutions:
6A) $(x+9)(x-5)$
6B) $(x+8)(x-4)$

EXAMPLE 7:
Factor.
7A) $x^2 + 12x + 36$
7B) $x^2 - 8x + 16$
Solutions:
7A) $(x+6)(x+6)$ or $(x+6)^2$
7B) $(x-4)(x-4)$ or $(x-4)^2$

EXAMPLE 8:
Factor.
8A) $x^2 - 4x - 77$
8B) $x^2 - 2x - 63$
Solutions:
8A) $(x-11)(x+7)$
8B) $(x-9)(x+7)$

EXAMPLE 9:
Factor.
9A) $x^2 + 10x + 20$
9B) $x^2 + 16x + 32$
Solutions:
9A) Prime   **9B)** Prime

EXAMPLE 10:
Factor.
10A) $m^2 + 2mn + n^2$
10B) $x^2 + 3xy + 2y^2$
Solutions:
10A) $(m+n)(m+n)$ or $(m+n)^2$
10B) $(x+2y)(x+y)$

EXAMPLE 11:
Factor.
11A) $x^2 - xy - 42y^2$
11B) $x^2 - xy - 30y^2$
Solutions:
11A) $(x+6y)(x-7y)$
11B) $(x+5y)(x-6y)$

EXAMPLE 12:
Factor.
12A) $2x^2 + 6x - 20$
12B) $3x^2 - 21x + 18$
Solutions:
12A) $2(x+5)(x-2)$
12B) $3(x-6)(x-1)$

EXAMPLE 13:
Factor.
13A) $2x^3 + 12x^2 - 54x$
13B) $3m^3 + 9m^2 - 84m$
Solutions:
13A) $2x(x+9)(x-3)$
13B) $3m(m+7)(m-4)$

Section 5.4
EXAMPLE 1:
Factor.
1A) $2x^2 - 5x - 12$
1B) $5x^2 - 33x - 14$
Solutions:
1A) $(2x+3)(x-4)$
1B) $(5x+2)(x-7)$

EXAMPLE 2:
Factor.
2A) $7x^2 - 11x - 6$
2B) $3x^2 - 5x - 12$
Solutions:
2A) $(7x+3)(x-2)$
2B) $(3x+4)(x-3)$

EXAMPLE 3:
Factor.
3A) $12x^2 + 37x + 3$
3B) $6x^2 + 31x + 5$
Solutions:
3A) $(12x+1)(x+3)$
3B) $(6x+1)(x+5)$

EXAMPLE 4:
Factor.
4A) $36x^2 - 12x + 1$
4B) $16x^2 - 8x + 1$
Solutions:
4A) $(6x-1)(6x-1)$ or $(6x-1)^2$
4B) $(4x-1)(4x-1)$ or $(4x-1)^2$

EXAMPLE 5:
Factor.
5A) $3x^2 + 7x + 1$
5B) $2x^2 + 11x + 7$
Solutions:
5A) Prime   **5B)** Prime

EXAMPLE 6:
Factor.
6A) $5x^2 + 7xy + 2y^2$
6B) $7x^2 + 10xy + 3y^2$
Solutions:
6A) $(5x+2y)(x+y)$
6B) $(7x+3y)(x+y)$

EXAMPLE 7:
Factor.
7A) $6x^2 - 19xy - 7y^2$
7B) $12x^2 - 37xy - 10y^2$
Solutions:
7A) $(2x-7y)(3x+y)$
7B) $(3x-10y)(4x+y)$

EXAMPLE 8:
Factor.
8A) $9x^3 + 15x^2 + 6x$
8B) $4x^3 + 38x^2 + 70x$
Solutions:
8A) $3x(3x+2)(x+1)$
8B) $2x(2x+5)(x+7)$

EXAMPLE 9:
Factor.
9A) $2x^2 + 13x + 15$
9B) $3x^2 + 14x + 15$
Solutions:
9A) $(x+5)(2x+3)$
9B) $(x+3)(3x+5)$

EXAMPLE 10:
Factor.
10A) $3x^2 - 7x - 6$
10B) $5x^2 - x - 22$
Solutions:
10A) $(x-3)(3x+2)$
10B) $(x+2)(5x-11)$

EXAMPLE 11:
Factor.
11A) $12x^2 + 37x + 3$
11B) $6x^2 + 31x + 5$
Solutions:
11A) $(x+3)(12x+1)$
11B) $(x+5)(6x+1)$

EXAMPLE 12
Factor.
12A) $49t^2 - 14t + 1$
12B) $121t^2 - 22t + 1$
Solutions:
12A) $(7t-1)(7t-1)$ or $(7t-1)^2$
12B) $(11t-1)(11t-1)$ or $(11t-1)^2$

EXAMPLE 13:
Factor.
13A) $3x^2 + 20x + 5$
13B) $5x^2 + 15x + 2$
Solutions:
13A) Prime   **13B)** Prime

EXAMPLE 14:
Factor.
14A) $5x^2 + 9xy + 4y^2$
14B) $7x^2 + 13xy + 6y^2$
Solutions:
14A) $(x+y)(5x+4y)$
14B) $(x+y)(7x+6y)$

EXAMPLE 15:
Factor.
15A) $14x^2 - 5xy - 6y^2$
15B) $6x^2 - 25xy - 9y^2$
Solutions:
15A) $(2x+y)(7x-6y)$
15B) $(3x+y)(2x-9y)$

EXAMPLE 16:
Factor.
16A) $6x^3 - 3x^2 - 30x$
16B) $6x^3 - 4x^2 - 66x$
Solutions:
16A) $3x(x+2)(2x-5)$
16B) $2x(x+3)(3x-11)$

Section 5.5
EXAMPLE 1:
Factor.
1A) $x^2 - 144$ **1B)** $x^2 - 169$
Solutions:
1A) $(x+12)(x-12)$
1B) $(x+13)(x-13)$

EXAMPLE 2:
Factor using the difference of two squares formula.
2A) $x^2 - 196$ **2B)** $x^2 - 256$
2C) $36x^2 - 49$ **2D)** $4x^2 - 9$
2E) $64x^2 - 9y^2$
2F) $49x^2 - 4y^2$
Solutions:
2A) $(x+14)(x-14)$
2B) $(x+16)(x-16)$
2C) $(6x+7)(6x-7)$
2D) $(2x+3)(2x-3)$
2E) $(8x+3)(8x-3)$
2F) $(7x+2)(7x-2)$

EXAMPLE 3:
Factor each difference of two squares.
3A) $81x^4 - 4y^4$
3B) $169x^4 - 9y^4$
3C) $x^8 - y^6$
3D) $x^6 - y^8$
Solutions:
3A) $(9x^2 + 2y^2)(9x^2 - 2y^2)$
3B) $(13x^2 + 3y^2)(13x^2 - 3y^2)$
3C) $(x^4 + y^3)(x^4 - y^3)$
3D) $(x^3 + y^4)(x^3 - y^4)$

EXAMPLE 4:
Factor using the difference of two squares formula.
4A) $9x^2 - 36y^2$
4B) $81x^2 - 9y^2$
Solutions:
4A) $9(x+2y)(x-2y)$
4B) $9(3x+y)(3x-y)$

EXAMPLE 5:
Factor using the difference of two squares formula.
5A) $x^4 - 256$ **5B)** $x^4 - 81$
Solutions:
5A) $(x^2 + 16)(x-4)(x+4)$
5B) $(x^2 + 9)(x-3)(x+3)$

EXAMPLE 6:
Factor.
6A) $x^3 + 125$ **6B)** $z^3 + 343$
Solutions:
6A) $(x+5)(x^2 - 5x + 25)$
6B) $(x+7)(x^2 - 7x + 49)$

EXAMPLE 7:
Factor.
7A) $z^3 - 343$ **7B)** $z^3 - 216$
Solutions:
7A) $(z-7)(z^2 + 7z + 49)$
7B) $(z-6)(z^2 + 6z + 36)$

EXAMPLE 8:
Factor.
8A) $216x^3 - y^3$ **8B)** $27m^3 - n^3$

Solutions:

8A) $(6x - y)(36x^2 + 6xy + y^2)$

8B) $(3m - n)(9m^2 + 3mn + n^2)$

EXAMPLE 9:
Factor.

9A) $27x^3 + 8y^3$

9B) $125x^3 + 27y^3$

Solutions:

9A) $(3x + 2y)(9x^2 - 6xy + 4y^2)$

9B) $(5x + 3y)(25x^2 - 15xy + 9y^2)$

EXAMPLE 10:
Factor.

10A) $2x^4 - 32x^2$

10B) $5x^4 - 405x^2$

Solutions:

10A) $2x^2(x + 4)(x - 4)$

10B) $5x^2(x + 9)(x - 9)$

EXAMPLE 11:
Factor.

11A) $5n^2m^2 + n^2m - 60n^2$

11B) $3p^2q^2 + 12p^2q - 36p^2$

Solutions:

11A) $5n^2(m + 4)(m - 3)$

11B) $3p^2(q + 6)(q - 2)$

EXAMPLE 12:
Factor.

12A) $6t^2r - 15tr + 21r$

12B) $3t^3r^2 - 12tr^2 + 15r^2$

Solutions:

12A) Prime   **12B)** Prime

EXAMPLE 13:
Factor.

13A) $5rt + 5r - 15t - 15$

13B) $3xy + 12x - 15y - 60$

Solutions:

13A) $5(r - 3)(t + 1)$

13B) $3(x - 5)(y + 4)$

EXAMPLE 14:
Factor.

14A) $45x^2 - 45x - 50$

14B) $50x^2 - 10x - 12$

Solutions:

14A) $5(3x + 2)(3x - 5)$

14B) $2(5x + 2)(5x - 3)$

EXAMPLE 15:
Factor.

15A) $3m^4n + 192mn$

15B) $5x^4y - 135xy$

Solutions:

15A) $3mn(m + 4)(m^2 - 4m + 16)$

15B) $5xy(x - 3)(x^2 + 3x + 9)$

Section 5.6

EXAMPLE 1:
Solve each equation.

1A) $(x + 7)(x + 4) = 0$

1B) $(x + 22)(x + 13) = 0$

Solutions:

1A) $x = -7, -4$

1B) $x = -22, -13$

EXAMPLE 2:
Solve each equation.

2A) $(2x + 5)(3x - 7) = 0$

2B) $(3x + 7)(2x - 11) = 0$

Solutions:

2A) $x = -\dfrac{5}{2}, \dfrac{7}{3}$

2B) $x = -\dfrac{7}{3}, \dfrac{11}{2}$

EXAMPLE 3:
Solve each equation.

3A) $4x^2 = 16x$

3B) $9x^2 = 27x$

Solutions:

3A) $x = 0, 4$ **3B)** $x = 0, 3$

EXAMPLE 4:
Solve each equation.

4A) $x^2 + 12x + 22 = 2$

4B) $x^2 + 11x + 34 = 4$

Solutions:

4A) $x = -10, -2$

4B) $x = -6, -5$

EXAMPLE 5:
Solve each equation.

5A) $5x^2 + 10x - 60 = -10x$

5B) $2x^2 - 5x - 24 = -3x$

Solutions:

5A) $x = -6, 2$ **5B)** $x = -3, 4$

EXAMPLE 6:
Solve each equation.

6A) $-x^2 + x + 6 = -0$

6B) $-x^2 + 4x + 12 = -0$

Solutions:

6A) $x = -2, 3$ **6B)** $x = -2, 6$

EXAMPLE 7:
Solve each equation.

7A) $x^2 = 144$ **7B)** $x^2 = 256$

Solutions:

7A) $x = \pm 12$ **7B)** $x = \pm 16$

EXAMPLE 8:
Solve each equation.

8A) $(x - 3)(x + 2) = 6$

8B) $(x - 5)(x + 2) = 8$

Solutions:

8A) $x = -3, 4$ **8B)** $x = -3, 6$

Section 5.7

EXAMPLE 1:

1A) The product of two numbers is 64. Find the two numbers if one number is 12 more than the other.

1B) The product of two numbers is 120. Find the two numbers if one number is 2 less than the other.

Solutions:

1A) 4 and 16   **1B)** 10 and 12

EXAMPLE 2:

2A) The length of a rectangular poster must be 4 units longer than its width. The poster must have an area of at least 96 square units. What must be the minimum dimensions of the poster?

2B) The area of a rectangle is 48 square feet. If the width of the rectangle is 13 feet less than the

length, find the dimensions of
the rectangle.
Solutions:
2A) 8 x 12 units   **2B)** 3 x 16 feet

EXAMPLE 3:
In Earth's gravitational field, the
distance d, in feet, that an object
released at rest falls after t
seconds can be found by the
formula $d = 16t^2$. Suppose an
object is dropped from the
heights defined below. How
long does it take the object to
reach the ground?
3A) 256 feet   **3B)** 144 feet
Solutions:
3A) 4 seconds   **3B)** 3 seconds

EXAMPLE 4:
Determine if a right triangle can
have the following sides.
4A) 6 inches, 8 inches, 10
inches
4B) 4 inches, 10 inches, 14
inches
4C) 5 feet, 12 feet, 13 feet
4D) 3 feet, 4 feet, 7 feet
Solutions:
4A) Yes   **4B)** No
4C) Yes   **4D)** No

EXAMPLE 5:
5A) One leg of a right triangle is
14 feet longer than the other leg.
The hypotenuse is 26 feet. Find
the dimensions of the right
triangle.
5B) One leg of a right triangle is
6 inches shorter than the
hypotenuse. The other leg is 12
inches. Find the lengths of the
other two sides of the right
triangle.
Solutions:
5A) The legs have measures 10
feet and 24 feet.
5B) One leg has measure 9
inches and the hypotenuse has
measure 15 inches.

EXAMPLE 6:
6A) Rick and Linda start riding
their bikes from the same place
at the same time. Rick heads
south while Linda heads east.
Rick rides 2 miles more than
Linda rides. At that instant the
distance between Rick and
Linda is 2 more than the
distance Rick has ridden. Find
the distance between Rick and
Linda.
6B) Two ships take off from the
same port at the same time. One
ship heads due south, while
another heads due west. The
ship heading south travels 4
miles more than twice the
distance that the other ship
travels. At that instant the
distance between the ships is 4
miles less than 3 times the
distance traveled by the ship
heading west. Find the distance
between the ships.
Solutions:
6A) 10 miles   **6B)** 26 miles

Chapter 6: Rational Expressions and Equations

Section 6.1

EXAMPLE 1:
Determine the values of x for which the following expressions are undefined.

1A) $\dfrac{x-4}{5x-3}$

1B) $\dfrac{x+7}{10x+5}$

1C) $\dfrac{x+6}{x^2-3x+2}$

1D) $\dfrac{x^2-5x+10}{x^2+3x-18}$

1E) $\dfrac{x-8}{x^2+x-12}$

1F) $\dfrac{x^2-16}{x^2-25}$

Solutions:

1A) $x \neq \dfrac{3}{5}$ **1B)** $x \neq -\dfrac{1}{2}$

1C) $x \neq 1, 2$ **1D)** $x \neq -6, 3$

1E) $x \neq -4, 3$ **1F)** $x \neq \pm 5$

EXAMPLE 2:
Simplify.

2A) $\dfrac{4x^3+8x^2-12x}{8x^2}$.

2B) $\dfrac{6y^4+12y^3-24y^2}{12y^2}$

Solutions:

2A) $\dfrac{x^2+2x-3}{2x}$

2B) $\dfrac{y^2+2y-4}{2}$

EXAMPLE 3:
Simplify.

3A) $\dfrac{x^2+3x-4}{x+4}$

3B) $\dfrac{x^2+x-30}{x-5}$

Solutions:

3A) $x-1$ **3B)** $x+6$

EXAMPLE 4:
Simplify.

4A) $\dfrac{x^2-25}{x+5}$ **4B)** $\dfrac{x^2-81}{x-9}$

Solutions:

4A) $x-5$ **4B)** $x+9$

EXAMPLE 5:
Simplify.

5A) $\dfrac{2x^2+9x+10}{x^2+3x+2}$

5B) $\dfrac{3x^2+14x+8}{x^2-3x-28}$

Solutions:

5A) $\dfrac{2x+5}{x+1}$ **5B)** $\dfrac{3x+2}{x-7}$

EXAMPLE 6:
Simplify.

6A) $\dfrac{2x-5}{5-2x}$ **6B)** $\dfrac{2x^2-5}{5-2x^2}$

Solutions:

6A) -1   **6B)** -1

EXAMPLE 7:
Simplify.

7A) $\dfrac{6x^2-29x+9}{1-3x}$

7B) $\dfrac{2x^2-21x+27}{9-x}$

Solutions:

7A) $-(2x-9)$ or $-2x+9$

7B) $-(2x-3)$ or $-2x+3$

Section 6.2

EXAMPLE 1:
Multiply.

1A) $\left(\dfrac{4}{7}\right)\left(\dfrac{14}{-12}\right)$

1B) $\left(\dfrac{5}{-6}\right)\left(\dfrac{24}{15}\right)$

Solutions:

1A) $-\dfrac{2}{3}$ **1B)** $-\dfrac{4}{3}$

EXAMPLE 2:
Multiply.

2A) $\dfrac{5x^2}{4y} \cdot \dfrac{6y^2}{5x}$

2B) $\dfrac{6x^3}{26y^2} \cdot \dfrac{13y^4}{6x}$

Solutions:

2A) $\dfrac{3xy}{2}$ **2B)** $\dfrac{x^2y^2}{2}$

EXAMPLE 3:
Multiply.

3A) $-\dfrac{2x^3}{5y^3} \cdot \dfrac{7y}{3x^5}$

3B) $-\dfrac{4x^2}{6y^5} \cdot \dfrac{11y}{2x^4}$

Solutions:

3A) $-\dfrac{14}{15x^2y^2}$ **3B)** $-\dfrac{11}{3x^2y^4}$

EXAMPLE 4:
Multiply.

4A) $(x-3) \cdot \dfrac{5}{x^4-3x^3}$

4B) $(x+5) \cdot \dfrac{7}{x^5+5x^4}$

Solutions:

4A) $\dfrac{5}{x^3}$ **4B)** $\dfrac{7}{x^4}$

EXAMPLE 5:
Multiply.

5A) $\dfrac{8x^2}{(x-2)^2} \cdot \dfrac{x^2-4}{4x^3}$

5B) $\dfrac{(x+3)^2}{9x^2} \cdot \dfrac{3x^5}{x^2-9}$

Solutions:

5A) $\dfrac{2x+4}{x(x-2)}$ 5B) $\dfrac{x^4+3x}{3(x-3)}$

EXAMPLE 6:
Multiply.

6A) $\dfrac{x-4}{3x} \cdot \dfrac{6x^2}{4-x}$

6B) $\dfrac{21x^3}{x-5} \cdot \dfrac{5-x}{7x}$

Solutions:

6A) $-2x$ 6B) $-3x^2$

EXAMPLE 7:
Multiply.

7A) $\dfrac{x+5}{4-6x} \cdot \dfrac{3x-2}{x+5}$

7B) $\dfrac{9-15x}{x-8} \cdot \dfrac{x-8}{5x-3}$

Solutions:

7A) $-\dfrac{1}{2}$ 7B) -2

EXAMPLE 8:
Multiply.

8A) $\dfrac{3x^2-13x-10}{3x^2+14x+8} \cdot \dfrac{3x^2+11x-4}{3x^2-16x+5}$

8B) $\dfrac{4x^2-8x-5}{2x^2-5x-3} \cdot \dfrac{2x^2+x-21}{4x^2+4x-35}$

Solutions:
8A) 1 8B) 1

EXAMPLE 9:
Multiply.

9A) $\dfrac{3x^3-15x^2+12x}{8y^3} \cdot \dfrac{-4y}{2x^2-2x}$

9B) $\dfrac{9y^4}{5x^3-35x^2+30x} \cdot \dfrac{5x^2-5x}{6y}$

Solutions:

9A) $\dfrac{-3x+12}{4y^2}$ 9B) $\dfrac{3y^3}{2(x-6)}$

EXAMPLE 10:
Multiply.

10A) $\dfrac{a^2-b^2}{a+b} \cdot \dfrac{a-2b}{2a^2-3ab+b^2}$

10B) $\dfrac{x-y}{3x^2-3y^2} \cdot \dfrac{3x^2+4xy+y^2}{y+3x}$

Solutions:

10A) $\dfrac{a-2b}{2a-b}$ 10B) $\dfrac{1}{3}$

EXAMPLE 11:
Divide:

11A) $\dfrac{2}{3} \div \dfrac{4}{3}$ 11B) $\dfrac{5}{6} \div \dfrac{5}{12}$

11C) $\dfrac{4}{7} \div \dfrac{5}{14}$ 11D) $\dfrac{15}{36} \div \dfrac{25}{18}$

Solutions:

11A) $\dfrac{1}{2}$ 11B) 2

11C) $\dfrac{8}{5}$ 11D) $\dfrac{3}{10}$

EXAMPLE 12:
Divide.

12A) $\dfrac{5y^3}{x} \div \dfrac{3x^3}{7}$

12B) $\dfrac{a^2}{7b^3} \div \dfrac{5b^3}{7a}$

Solutions:

12A) $\dfrac{35y^3}{3x^4}$ 12B) $\dfrac{a^3}{5b^6}$

EXAMPLE 13:
Divide.

13A) $\dfrac{x^2-4}{x+5} \div \dfrac{x+4}{x+5}$

13B) $\dfrac{x-7}{x+4} \div \dfrac{x-7}{x^2-16}$

Solutions:
13A) $x-4$ 13B) $x-4$

EXAMPLE 14:
Divide.

14A) $\dfrac{-1}{3x-5} \div \dfrac{4}{5-3x}$

14B) $\dfrac{4x-7}{-1} \div \dfrac{7-4x}{-2}$

Solutions:

14A) $\dfrac{1}{4}$ 14B) 2

EXAMPLE 15:
Divide.

15A) $\dfrac{x^2+6x+8}{x^3} \div (x+2)^2$

15B) $\dfrac{x^2+4x-21}{x^2} \div (x-3)^2$

Solutions:

15A) $\dfrac{x+4}{x^3(x+2)}$ 15B) $\dfrac{x+7}{x^2(x-3)}$

EXAMPLE 16:
Divide.

16A) $\dfrac{6x^2+15x-36}{2x} \div \dfrac{2x^2-x-3}{4x^2+4x}$

16B) $\dfrac{6x^2+41x-30}{2x} \div \dfrac{3x^2+16x-12}{6x^2+36x}$

Solutions:
16A) $6x+24$ 16B) $6x+45$

Section 6.3
EXAMPLE 1:

1A) Add $\dfrac{8}{19}+\dfrac{7}{19}$.

1B) Add $\dfrac{8}{18}+\dfrac{7}{18}$.

1C) Subtract $\dfrac{6}{7}-\dfrac{3}{7}$

1D) Subtract $\dfrac{8}{24}-\dfrac{6}{24}$

Solutions:

1A) $\dfrac{15}{19}$ 1B) $\dfrac{5}{6}$

1C) $\dfrac{3}{7}$ 1D) $\dfrac{1}{12}$

EXAMPLE 2:
Add.

2A) $\dfrac{x+2}{x-6}+\dfrac{13}{x-6}$

2B) $\dfrac{x}{x+8}+\dfrac{x+15}{x+8}$

Solutions:

2A) $\dfrac{x+15}{x-6}$ **2B)** $\dfrac{2x+15}{x+8}$

EXAMPLE 3:
Add.

3A) $\dfrac{3x^2+3x}{x+2}+\dfrac{2x-4}{x+2}$

3B) $\dfrac{2x^3+3x^2}{x-4}+\dfrac{x-3}{x-4}$

Solutions:

3A) $\dfrac{3x^2+5x-4}{x+2}$

3B) $\dfrac{2x^3+3x^2+x-3}{x-4}$

EXAMPLE 4:
Add.

4A) $\dfrac{x^2+3x-3}{(x-2)(x+7)}+\dfrac{x-18}{(x-2)(x+7)}$

4B) $\dfrac{x^2+3x-3}{(x+1)(x+5)}+\dfrac{8x+11}{(x+1)(x+5)}$

Solutions:

4A) $\dfrac{x-3}{x-2}$ **4B)** $\dfrac{x+7}{x+5}$

EXAMPLE 5:
Subtract.

5A) $\dfrac{x^2-4x-3}{x^2+7x+10}-\dfrac{x^2-6x-7}{x^2+7x+10}$

5B) $\dfrac{x^2+7x-13}{x^2+8x+12}-\dfrac{x^2+8x-7}{x^2+8x+12}$

Solutions:

5A) $\dfrac{2}{(x+5)}$ **5B)** $-\dfrac{1}{x+2}$

EXAMPLE 6:
Subtract.

6A) $\dfrac{-8x}{x+3}-\dfrac{2x^2-7x-15}{x+3}$

6B) $\dfrac{7x}{x+2}-\dfrac{-3x^2+2x+2}{x+2}$

Solutions:

6A) $-2x-5$ **6B)** $3x-1$

EXAMPLE 7:
Add.

7A) $\dfrac{2}{5}+\dfrac{4}{9}$ **7B)** $\dfrac{3}{8}+\dfrac{5}{9}$

Solutions:

7A) $\dfrac{38}{45}$ **7B)** $\dfrac{67}{72}$

EXAMPLE 8:
Find the least common denominator.

8A) $\dfrac{7}{x}+\dfrac{3}{2}$ **8B)** $\dfrac{8}{a}-\dfrac{7}{b}$

Solutions:

8A) $2x$ **8B)** ab

EXAMPLE 9:
Find the LCD.

9A) $\dfrac{8x}{7x}-\dfrac{10}{x^2}$

9B) $\dfrac{3}{17x^2}+\dfrac{11x}{x^3}$

Solutions:

9A) $7x^2$ **9B)** $17x^3$

EXAMPLE 10:
Find the LCD.

10A) $\dfrac{2}{15x^3y}+\dfrac{1}{18x^2y^3}$

10B) $\dfrac{12}{24x^4y^2}-\dfrac{x}{36xy^2}$

Solutions:

10A) $90x^3y^3$ **10B)** $72x^4y^2$

EXAMPLE 11:
Find the LCD.

11A) $\dfrac{10}{y}-\dfrac{12x}{y+2}$

11B) $\dfrac{x}{x+5}+\dfrac{3x}{x}$

Solutions:

11A) $y(y+2)$ **11B)** $x(x+5)$

EXAMPLE 12:
Find the LCD.

12A) $\dfrac{6}{4x^2-12x}+\dfrac{2x^2}{x^2-6x+9}$

12B) $\dfrac{42}{x^2+10x+25}-\dfrac{5x^2}{2x^2+10x}$

Solutions:

12A) $4x(x-3)^2$

12B) $2x(x+5)^2$

EXAMPLE 13:
Find the LCD.

13A) $\dfrac{4}{x^2-8x+15}-\dfrac{5x}{x^2+2x-15}$

13B) $\dfrac{3x}{x^2+11x+30}+\dfrac{7}{x^2+15x+56}$

Solutions:

13A) $(x-5)(x-3)(x+5)$

13B) $(x+5)(x+6)(x+7)(x+8)$

EXAMPLE 14:
Find the LCD.

14A) $\dfrac{8x}{x^2-10x+21}+x+4$

14B) $x-8+\dfrac{8x}{x^2+14x+40}$

Solutions:

14A) $(x-3)(x-7)$

14B) $(x+4)(x+10)$

Section 6.4
EXAMPLE 1:
Add.

1A) $\dfrac{6}{r}+\dfrac{7}{s}$ **1B)** $\dfrac{4}{y}+\dfrac{12}{x}$

Solutions:

1A) $\dfrac{6s+7r}{rs}$ **1B)** $\dfrac{4x+12y}{xy}$

EXAMPLE 2:
Add.

2A) $\dfrac{7}{6x^3y^2}+\dfrac{5}{16xy}$

2B) $\dfrac{1}{18x^2y^3}+\dfrac{3}{24x^3y^2}$

Solutions:

2A) $\dfrac{56+15x^2y}{48x^3y^2}$

2B) $\dfrac{4x+3y}{72x^3y^2}$

EXAMPLE 3:
Add.

3A) $\dfrac{3}{x+6}+\dfrac{7}{x}$ **3B)** $\dfrac{5}{y}+\dfrac{11}{y-2}$

Solutions:

3A) $\dfrac{10x+42}{x(x+6)}$ 3B) $\dfrac{16y-10}{y(y-2)}$

EXAMPLE 4:
Subtract.

4A) $\dfrac{x}{x-3}-\dfrac{7}{x-2}$

4B) $\dfrac{4}{g+5}-\dfrac{g}{g+3}$

Solutions:

4A) $\dfrac{x^2-9x+21}{(x-3)(x-2)}$

4B) $\dfrac{-g^2-g+12}{(g+5)(g+3)}$

EXAMPLE 5:
Subtract.

5A) $\dfrac{x-3}{x+2}-\dfrac{x+5}{x-2}$

5B) $\dfrac{x-2}{x-6}-\dfrac{x+7}{x+6}$

Solutions:

5A) $\dfrac{-12x-10}{(x+2)(x-2)}$

5B) $\dfrac{3x+30}{(x+6)(x-6)}$

EXAMPLE 6:
Add.

6A) $\dfrac{9}{x-1}+\dfrac{x+2}{1-x}$

6B) $\dfrac{-2x-5}{x-5}+\dfrac{x-3}{5-x}$

Solutions:

6A) $\dfrac{7-x}{x-1}$ 6B) $\dfrac{-2-3x}{x-5}$

EXAMPLE 7:
Subtract.

7A) $\dfrac{x+7}{2x-5}-\dfrac{3x-2}{5-2x}$

7B) $\dfrac{5x-7}{7x-1}-\dfrac{-x-6}{1-7x}$

Solutions:

7A) $\dfrac{4x+9}{2x-5}$ 7B) $\dfrac{4x-13}{7x-1}$

EXAMPLE 8:
Add.

8A) $\dfrac{2}{x^2+4x+3}+\dfrac{1}{3x^2+x-2}$

8B) $\dfrac{-3}{4x^2+19x-5}+\dfrac{2}{x^2+2x-15}$

Solutions:

8A) $\dfrac{7x-1}{(x+1)(x+3)(3x-2)}$

8B) $\dfrac{5x+7}{(4x-1)(x+5)(x-3)}$

EXAMPLE 9:

9A) $\dfrac{4}{x^2-4x}-\dfrac{x}{4x-16}$

9B) $\dfrac{3}{x^2-3x}-\dfrac{x^2}{9x-27}$

Solutions:

9A) $\dfrac{-x-4}{4x}$

9B) $\dfrac{-x^2-3x-9}{9x}$

Section 6.5

EXAMPLE 1:
Simplify.

1A) $\dfrac{\frac{a^2b}{c^4}}{\frac{ab}{c}}$ 1B) $\dfrac{\frac{x^2y^2}{z^2}}{\frac{xz^3}{y}}$

Solutions:

1A) $\dfrac{a}{c^3}$ 1B) $\dfrac{xy^3}{z^5}$

EXAMPLE 2:
Simplify:

2A) $\dfrac{x+\frac{1}{y}}{y+\frac{1}{x}}$ 2B) $\dfrac{a-\frac{1}{b}}{b-\frac{1}{a}}$

Solutions:

2A) $\dfrac{x}{y}$ 2B) $\dfrac{a}{b}$

EXAMPLE 3:
Simplify.

3A) $\dfrac{\frac{1}{4}+\frac{5}{6}}{\frac{3}{4}-\frac{1}{2}}$ 3B) $\dfrac{\frac{5}{7}-\frac{1}{6}}{\frac{6}{7}-\frac{1}{3}}$

Solutions:

3A) $\dfrac{13}{3}$ 3B) $\dfrac{23}{22}$

EXAMPLE 4:
Rework Example 2 using
"method 2".

4A) $\dfrac{x+\frac{1}{y}}{y+\frac{1}{x}}$ 4B) $\dfrac{a-\frac{1}{b}}{b-\frac{1}{a}}$

Solutions:

4A) $\dfrac{x}{y}$ 4B) $\dfrac{a}{b}$

EXAMPLE 5:
Simplify.

5A) $\dfrac{a}{\frac{1}{a}+\frac{1}{b}}$ 5B) $\dfrac{\frac{1}{x}-\frac{1}{y}}{x}$

Solutions:

5A) $\dfrac{a^2b}{a+b}$ 5B) $\dfrac{y-x}{x^2y}$

Section 6.6

EXAMPLE 1:
Solve.

1A) $\dfrac{x}{2}-\dfrac{x}{3}=1$ 1B) $\dfrac{x}{2}+\dfrac{x}{3}=2$

Solutions:

1A) $x=6$ 1B) $x=\dfrac{12}{5}$

EXAMPLE 2:
Solve.

1A) $\dfrac{x-2}{20}=\dfrac{3}{4}-\dfrac{x-5}{10}$

2B) $\dfrac{x+1}{15}=\dfrac{9}{45}-\dfrac{x+2}{9}$

Solutions:

2A) $x=9$ 2B) $x=-\dfrac{1}{2}$

EXAMPLE 3:
Solve each equation.

3A) $4 - \dfrac{9}{x} = \dfrac{3}{2}$ **3B)** $9 = \dfrac{4}{x} + \dfrac{2}{3}$

Solutions:

3A) $x = \dfrac{18}{5}$ **3B)** $x = \dfrac{12}{25}$

EXAMPLE 4:
Solve each equation.

4A) $\dfrac{x+4}{x-2} = \dfrac{1}{6}$ **4B)** $\dfrac{r+7}{r+3} = \dfrac{1}{8}$

Solutions:

4A) $x = -\dfrac{26}{5}$ **4B)** $x = -\dfrac{53}{7}$

EXAMPLE 5:
Use cross-multiplication to solve each equation.

5A) $\dfrac{7}{r+4} = \dfrac{6}{r+5}$

5B) $\dfrac{1}{x-6} = \dfrac{4}{x-9}$

Solutions:

5A) x = -11 **5B)** x = 5

EXAMPLE 6:
Solve each equation.

6A) $x + \dfrac{9}{x} = -6$

6B) $x - \dfrac{20}{x} = 1$

Solutions:

6A) x = -3 **6B)** x = -4, 5

EXAMPLE 7:
Solve each equation.

7A) $\dfrac{x^2 + x}{x+1} = \dfrac{12}{x+1}$

7B) $\dfrac{-6}{x-3} = \dfrac{x^2 + 5x}{x-3}$

Solutions:

7A) $x = -4, 3$

7B) $x = -3, -2$

EXAMPLE 8:
Solve each equation.

8A) $\dfrac{6x}{x^2 - 9} + \dfrac{1}{x-3} = \dfrac{3}{x+3}$

8B) $\dfrac{2}{x+4} + \dfrac{x}{x-4} = \dfrac{19}{x^2 - 16}$

Solutions:

8A) x = -3 **8B)** x = -9, 3

Section 6.7
EXAMPLE 1:
1A) The width of a rectangular rug is 4 feet less than $\frac{2}{3}$ the length of the rug. If the area of the rug is 90 square feet, find the dimensions of the rug.
1B) The length of a playing field is 6 feet more than 1.5 times its width. If the area of the field is 15,600 square feet, find the dimensions of the field.
Solutions:
1A) 6 feet by 15 feet
1B) 100 feet by 156 feet

EXAMPLE 2:
2A) One number is 2 times another number. The sum of their reciprocals is $\frac{12}{5}$. Determine the numbers.
2B) One number is 4 times another number. The difference of their reciprocals is 5. Determine the numbers.
Solutions:

2A) $\dfrac{5}{8}$ and $\dfrac{5}{4}$

2B) $\dfrac{3}{20}$ and $\dfrac{3}{5}$

EXAMPLE 3:
3A) Robert is in his boat fishing in a stream that has a 3 mph current. He can go downstream 12 miles in the same amount of time it takes him to go upstream 3 miles. Determine the speed of Robert's boat.
3B) Meg is riding her bike on a north-south road. The wind is blowing from the south at a speed of 10 mph. Meg can ride 18 miles north in the same amount of time she can ride 6 miles south. At what speed

would Meg be traveling if there was no wind?
Solutions:
3A) 5 mph **3B)** 20 mph

EXAMPLE 4:
4A) During a usual morning run, Marcy ran uphill averaging 4 mph and then downhill averaging 6mph. Marcy ran a total of 6 miles. She completes her run in 75 minutes. How long did she run at each speed?
4B) The United Express Mountain Train makes a daily 30-mile route for tourists. On this route exists a 9-mile section in which the train makes an ascent up a small mountain, then descends again. The train's speed up the mountain is 20 mph. The speed down the mountain is 40 mph. This section of the route takes 21 minutes for the train to complete. How long does the train travel at each speed?
Solutions:
4A) 45 minutes at 4 mph and 30 minutes at 6 mph
4B) 15 minutes at 20 mph and 6 min at 40 mph

EXAMPLE 5:
5A) Many ultra-marathon road runs offer opportunities for teams of 4 runners to run the distance. At a recent ultra-marathon event, Gene completed the run individually at an average pace of 5 mph. Four his friends teamed up to finish the run at an average pace of 8 mph. The team completed the run 3.75 hours sooner than Gene. Find the distance of this ultra-marathon.
5B) Maggie and Martha are twin sisters attending the same college. When Maggie drives home to see her parents, her average speed is 60 mph. Martha however averages 70 mph when she drives home. It takes Maggie 1 hour more to get home than it takes Martha. Find

the distance from their college to their hometown.
Solutions:
5A) 50 miles   **5B)** 420 miles

EXAMPLE 6:
6A) Fred can paint an average-sized house by himself in 40 hours. His partner Rebecca can paint the same-sized house by herself in 35 hours. How long will it take them to paint an average-sized house if they work together?
6B) David can rake the leaves in his yard in 2 hours. His sister can rake the same leaves in 3 hours. How long would it take for them to complete the task together?
Solutions:

6A) $18 \frac{2}{3}$ hours

6B) 1.2 hours

EXAMPLE 7:
7A) A certain bathtub can be filled in 10 minutes and drained in 6 minutes. If the water is running and the drain is open, how long will it take for the tub to empty?
7B) At a local soda-bottling factory, a pipe leading into a tank can fill it with soda in 2 hours and another can empty the tank in 3 hours. If the valves to both pipes are open, how long will it take to fill the tank?
Solutions:
7A) 15 minutes   **7B)** 6 hours

EXAMPLE 8:
8A) Phyllis and Janine can clean the McCarthy's house in 3 hours. When Phyllis cleans the McCarthy's house by herself, it takes 5 hours. How long does it take Janine to clean the McCarthy's house herself?
8B) The Harris' basement recently filled completely with water after a flash flood. In order to drain their basement, they use a pump that can drain all of the water in 10 hours. In

order to speed up the process, the Harris' use buckets to take water from the basement. Together with the pump, the Harris' are able to rid their basement of water in 8 hours. If they did not have the pump, how long would it have taken them to remove the water from their basement?
Solutions:
8A) 7.5 hours   **8B)** 40 hours

EXAMPLE 9:
9A) Danielle begins painting her house and spends 10 hours during the first two days of the project. During the second day, Danielle falls off a ladder and cannot finish the project. Her sister Denise finishes the project for her. Danielle could have painted the entire house in 20 hours. Denise could paint the entire house in 30 hours. How long will it take Denise to finish painting the house?
9B) After a wedding celebration at the Millard Social Hall, Winona and Jean are in charge of cleaning the hall. There are many dishes that need washing and Winona begins this task. She knows she can complete the work in 2.5 hours. After 45 minutes of washing dishes, Winona becomes ill and must leave. Jean completes the dish-washing job. Jean knows that it would have taken her 2 hours to complete the job. How long does it take her to complete the job after the time she began?
Solutions:
9A) 15 hours   **9B)** 1.4 hours

Section 6.8
EXAMPLE 1:
1A) When a cup of water is put in the microwave, the temperature of the water, x, increases directly with the time, t, the microwave is on. **a)** Write the variation as an equation. **b)**

If the constant of proportionality, k, is 35, find the increase in temperature of the water after 5 minutes.
1B) The cost of renting a car, c, is directly proportional to the number of miles, m, driven by the customer (assume the cost only includes a mileage fee). **a)** Write the variation as an equation. **b)** If the constant of proportionality is 0.4, find the cost of the rental after the customer has driven 200 miles.
Solutions:
1A) a) $x = kt$; **b)** After 5 minutes the temperature of the water has increased by 175°.
1B) a) $c = km$; **b)** $80

EXAMPLE 2:
Suppose x varies directly as the square of y.
2A) If $x = 144$ when $y = 6$, find x when $y = 36$.
2B) If $x = 20$ when $y = 40$, find x when $y = 100$
Solutions:
2A) 5184   **2B)** 125

EXAMPLE 3:
3A) The amount of calories that a person should consume is directly proportional to the person's weight. If a person who weighs 150 pounds should consume 1800 calories per day, determine how many calories a person should consume who weighs 180 pounds.
3B) The time it takes for Sam to paint is directly proportional to the surface area of the shed. If it takes Sam 2 hours to paint his shed which has a surface area of 400 square feet, how long will it take him to paint his house which has a surface area of 3200 square feet.
Solutions:
3A) 2160 calories
3B) 16 hours

EXAMPLE 4:

4A) A group of friends is going to rent a condo for an upcoming ski trip to Colorado. The cost per person for renting the condo is inversely proportional to the number of people staying in the condo. If 6 friends decide to rent the condo, the cost per person is $50. Determine the cost per person if 10 friends decide to rent the condo.

4B) The time it takes for Dawn to travel on the interstate is inversely proportional to the speed at which Dawn is driving. If Dawn drives at an average speed of 65 mph, it takes her 5 hours to reach her destination. Determine the speed at which Dawn must average if she wishes to make the trip in 4.5 hours.

Solutions:

4A) $30 per person

4B) Approximately 72 mph

EXAMPLE 5:

5A) For a cone of specific volume, the height, h, of the cone is inversely proportional to the square of the radius of the cone, r. When the radius is 3 feet, the height is 10 feet. Determine the height when the radius is 4 feet.

5B) The loudness of a sound, measured in decibels (dB), varies inversely as the square of the distance of the listener from the sound. Suppose the loudness of a certain sound is 10 dB when the listener is 8 feet from the sound. Determine the loudness when a person is 2 feet from the sound.

Solutions:

5A) 5.625 feet   **5B)** 160 dB

Chapter 7: Graphing Linear Equations

Section 7.1
EXAMPLE 1:
Plot each point on the same axis.
1A) J(3, 5)   **1B)** K(5, 3)
1C) L(-2, 5)   **1D)** M(3, 0)
1E) N(-1, -3)   **1F)** P(0, -2)

1G) Q(0, 5)   **1H)** R$\left(2, \dfrac{5}{2}\right)$

1I) T$\left(\dfrac{7}{2}, -\dfrac{3}{2}\right)$

Solutions:

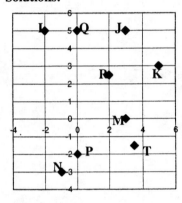

EXAMPLE 2:
List the ordered pairs for each point shown in the figure below.

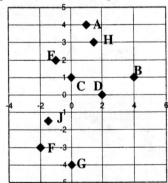

Solutions:

A(1, 4)   B(4, 1)
C(0, 1)   D(2, 0)
E(-1, 2)   F(-2, -3)

G(0, -4)   H$\left(\dfrac{3}{2}, 3\right)$

J$\left(-\dfrac{3}{2}, -\dfrac{3}{2}\right)$

EXAMPLE 3:
Determine whether the three points given appear to be collinear.
3A) (0, 4), (1.5, 0), (-3, -2)
3B) (7, 3), (3, 8), (9, 0.5)
3C) (-8, 5), (0, 10), (5, 15)
Solutions:
3A) No   **3B)** Yes
3C) Yes

EXAMPLE 4:
4A) a) Determine which of the following ordered pairs satisfy the equation $3x + 4y = 14$.
(3, 4), (2, 2), (-2, 5), (0, 6)
b) Plot all the points that satisfy the equation on the same axis, and draw a straight line through the points. **c)** What does this straight line represent?
4B) a) Determine which of the following ordered pairs satisfy the equation $-3x - 5y = -13$.
(1, 2), (-1, -2), (6, -1), (0, 3)
b) Plot all the points that satisfy the equation on the same axis, and draw a straight line through the points. **c)** What does this straight line represent?
Solutions:
4A) a) (2, 2) and (-2, 5);
b)

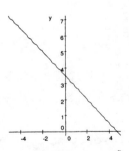

c) All of the solutions to the equation $3x + 4y = 14$.
4B) a) (1, 2) and (6, -1);

b)

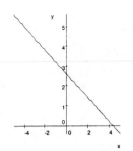

c) All of the solutions to the equation $-3x - 5y = -13$.

Section 7.2
EXAMPLE 1:
Graph each equation.
1A) $y = 4x + 2$ **1B)** $y = 3x - 9$
Solutions:
1A)

1B)

EXAMPLE 2:
Graph each equation.
2A) $3y = 6x - 15$
2B) $2y = -3x - 18$
Solutions:
2A)

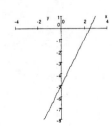

2B)

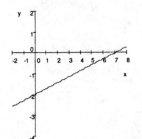

4B)

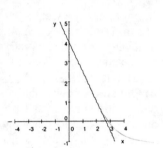

6B)

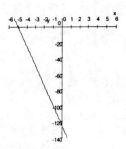

EXAMPLE 3:
Graph each equation.
3A) $3x + 7y = 0$
3B) $8x + 3y = 0$
Solutions:
3A)

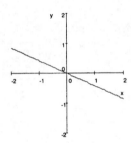

3B)

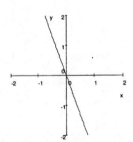

EXAMPLE 4:
Graph each equation by plotting
the x- and y-intercepts.
4A) $4y = 8x + 16$
4B) $7y = 2x - 14$
Solutions:
4A)

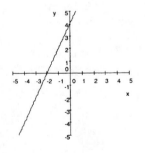

EXAMPLE 5:
Graph each equation by finding
the x- and y-intercepts.
5A) $3x + 2y = 8$
5B) $3x - 5y = 12$
Solutions:
5A)

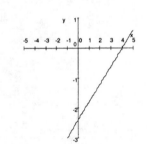

5B)

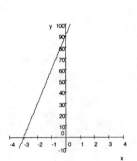

EXAMPLE 6:
Graph each equation.
6A) $y = 30x + 90$
6B) $y = -25x - 125$
Solutions:
6A)

EXAMPLE 7:
Graph each equation.
7A) $y = 8.$ **7B)** $y = -3.$
Solutions:
7A)

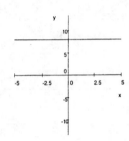

7B)

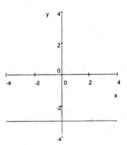

EXAMPLE 8:
Graph each equation.
8A) $x = -3$ **8B)** $x = 10$
Solutions:
8A)

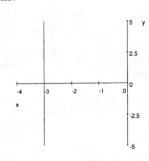

8B)

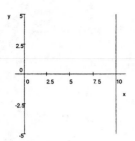

EXAMPLE 9:
9A) John Smith recently accepted a position as a sales representative at an electronics store. He is paid a bi-weekly salary plus commission on sales. He will receive a salary of $400 every two weeks plus 6% commission on all sales, s.
a) Write an equation for the salary, R, John will receive, in terms of the sales, s. **b)** Graph the salary for sales from $0 up to and including $15,000. **c)** From the graph, estimate the salary if John's bi-weekly sales are $10,000. **d)** From the graph, estimate the sales needed for John to earn a bi-weekly salary of $2000.
9B) The cost of playing at the Crestline Golf Club is a $500 yearly membership fee plus $25 green fees every time the member plays golf. **a)** Write an equation for the cost, C, that a member will pay, in terms of the number of times the member plays golf, n. **b)** Graph the cost for playing n rounds from 0 to 100. **c)** From the graph, estimate the cost to a member if he plays 25 rounds of golf. **d)** If a member spends $2300.
Solutions:
9A) a) R = 400 + 0.06s;

b)

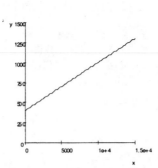

c) $1,000; **d)** Approximately $26,667
9B) a) C = 500 + 25n;
b)

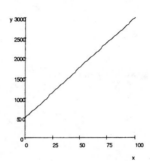

c) $1125; **d)** 72 rounds

Section 7.3
EXAMPLE 1:
1A) Find the slope of the line through the points (-2, -4) and (4, 7).
1B) Find the slope of the line through the points (3, 10) and (-3, -2).
Solutions:

1A) $\dfrac{11}{6}$ **1B)** 2

EXAMPLE 2:
2A) a) Plot the points (-3, -1) and (-1, 2) and draw a line through these points. Find the slope of the line by observing the vertical change and horizontal change between these points. **b)** Calculate the slope of the line using the two given points.

2B) a) Plot the points (1, 3) and (-1, 6) and draw a line through these points. Find the slope of the line by observing the vertical change and horizontal change between these points. **b)** Calculate the slope of the line using the two given points.
Solutions:
2A)
a)

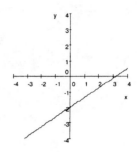

b) $m = \dfrac{3}{2}$

2B)
a)

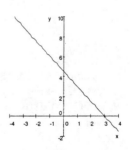

b) $m = -\dfrac{3}{2}$

EXAMPLE 3:
3A) Plot the points (-3, 1) and (2, 11) and draw a line through these points. Find the slope of the line by observing the vertical change and horizontal change between these points.
3B) Plot the points (2, 7) and (-5, 7) and draw a line through these points. Find the slope of the line by observing the vertical change and horizontal change between these points.

Solutions:

3A)

a)

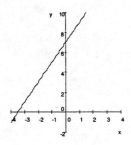

b) $m = 2$

3B)

a)

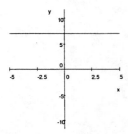

b) $m = 0$

EXAMPLE 4:
4A) Refer to Example 4 on page 466 of your text. Use the points (1994, 279) and (2000, 290) to find the slope of the red line.
4B) Refer to Exercise 71 on page 472 of your text. Use the points (55, 81) and (7, 85) to find the slope of the line connecting these points.
Solutions:

4A) $m = \dfrac{7}{2}$ **4B)** $m = -\dfrac{1}{16}$

EXAMPLE 5:
5A) **a)** Draw a line with a slope of $\frac{2}{3}$ through the point (0, -2).
b) On the same set of axis, draw a line with a slope of $\frac{2}{3}$ through the point (-3, 6). **c)** Are the two lines in part a) and b) parallel? Explain.

5B) **a)** Draw a line with a slope of 5 through the point (-3, 2).
b) On the same set of axis, draw a line with a slope of $-\frac{1}{5}$ through the point (3, 0). **c)** Are the two lines in part a) and b) parallel? Explain.
Solutions:
5A)
a,b)

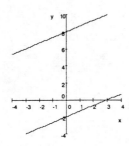

c) Yes, they have the same slopes.
5B)
a,b)

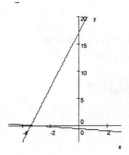

c) No, they do not have the same slopes.

EXAMPLE 6:
6A) **a)** Draw a line with a slope of 5 through the point (-1, -2).
b) On the same set of axis, draw a line with a slope of $-\frac{1}{5}$ through the point (0, 2).
c) Are the two lines in parts a) and b) perpendicular? Explain.
6B) **a)** Draw a line with a slope of $\frac{2}{3}$ through the point (0, 4).

b) On the same set of axis, draw a line with a slope of $-\frac{2}{3}$ through the point (0, 2).
c) Are the two lines in parts a) and b) perpendicular? Explain.
Solutions:
6A)
a,b)

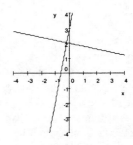

c) Yes, their slopes are negative reciprocals.
6B)
a,b)

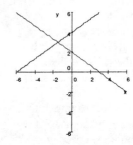

c) No, their slopes are not negative reciprocals.

EXAMPLE 7:
If m_1 represents the slope of line 1 and m_2 represents the slope of line 2, determine if line 1 and 2 are parallel, perpendicular, or neither.

7A) $m_1 = \frac{2}{3}$ and $m_2 = \frac{3}{2}$

7B) $m_1 = -3$ and $m_2 = \frac{1}{3}$

7C) $m_1 = \frac{3}{4}$ and $m_2 = \frac{3}{4}$

7D) $m_1 = 0.3$ and $m_2 = \frac{1}{3}$

7E) $m_1 = \frac{5}{8}$ and $m_2 = 0.625$

7F) $m_1 = -\frac{2}{3}$ and $m_2 = \frac{6}{4}$

Solutions:
7A) Neither
7B) Perpendicular
7C) Parallel
7D) Neither
7E) Parallel
7F) Perpendicular

Section 7.4
EXAMPLE 1:
Write each equation in slope-intercept form. State the slope and y-intercept.
1A) $-4x + 5y = 8$
1B) $9x - 6y = 12$
Solutions:

1A) $y = \frac{4}{5}x + \frac{8}{5}$; slope $= \frac{4}{5}$;

y-intercept $= \frac{8}{5}$

1B) $y = \frac{3}{2}x - 2$; slope $= \frac{3}{2}$;

y-intercept $= -2$

EXAMPLE 2:
Determine whether the two equations represent lines that are parallel, perpendicular, or neither.
2A) $3x + 2y = 5$ and $-6x = 4y - 10$

2B) $y = \frac{3}{5}x - 2$ and

$5x + 3y = 3$

2C) $y = \frac{2}{7}x - 5$ and

$2x + 6y = 10$

2D $2x + 6y = 9$ and

$12x + 4y = 10$

Solutions:
2A) Parallel
2B) Perpendicular
2C) Neither
2D) Neither

EXAMPLE 3:
Write each equation in slope-intercept form; then use the slope and y-intercept to graph each equation.
3A) $-4x + 7y = 14$
3B) $5x - 8y = 16$
Solutions:

3A) $y = \frac{4}{7}x + 2$

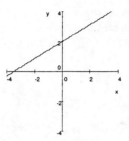

3B) $y = \frac{5}{8}x - 2$

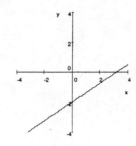

EXAMPLE 4:
Graph each equation by using the slope and y-intercept.
4A) $3x + 5y = 10$
4B) $-4x - 2y = 12$
Solutions:
4A)

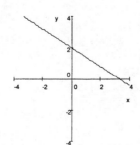

4B)

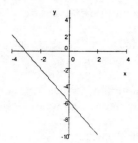

EXAMPLE 5:
Determine the equation of each of the lines shown.
5A)

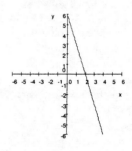

5B)

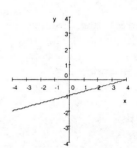

Solutions:
5A) $y = -3x + 6$

5B) $y = +\frac{1}{4}x - 1$

EXAMPLE 6:
6A) Gena Palmari bakes different types of breads and sells them out of her home. Each loaf costs $4.00. Her set cost per month of running her business averages to $100. **a)** Find the equation of the total monthly profit, P, when n loafs

are sold. **b)** Use the equation found in part a) to find the total monthly profit if 50 loafs are sold. **c)** Graph the equation in part a) and use it to check your answer in part b).

6B) On a trip across the country, Allison Murphy decides that she will keep track of her total distance traveled. She decides this after she has already traveled 300 miles. She figures that she will average a speed of 60 mph during the rest of her trip. **a)** Write an equation for the distance, D, in terms of the time, t, in hours, that describes Allison's trip. **b)** Use the equation found in part a) to find the total distance traveled if Allison drives for 12 hours (after driving the initial 300 miles). **c)** Graph the equation in part a) and use it to check your answer in part b).

Solutions:
6A) a) P = 4n - 100; **b)** $100
6B) a) D = 300 + 60t; **b)** 1020 miles

EXAMPLE 7:
Write an equation, in slope-intercept form, of the line that goes through the given point and has the given slope.
7A) (4, 2) and 6
7B) (-2, -1) and −1
Solutions:
1A) y = 6x − 22   **1B)** y = -x − 3

EXAMPLE 8:
Write an equation, in slope-intercept form, of the line that goes through the given point and has the given slope.

8A) (-4, 2) and $3/2$

8B) (1, 6) and $-1/4$

Solutions:

8A) $y = \dfrac{3}{2}x + 8$

8B) $y = -\dfrac{1}{4}x + \dfrac{25}{4}$

EXAMPLE 9:
Find an equation of the line through the given points. Write the equation in slope-intercept form.
9A) (-2, -5) and (2, 1)
9B) (3, 6) and (2, 3)
Solutions:

9A) $y = \dfrac{3}{2}x - 2$ **9B)** y = 3x − 3

EXAMPLE 10:
Graph each equation **a)** by plotting points; **b)** using the x- and y-intercepts; and **c)** using the slope and y-intercept.
10A) 4x − 2y = 16
10B) −6x − 3y = 15
Solutions:
10A)

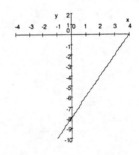

10B)

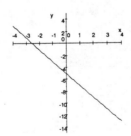

Section 7.5
EXAMPLE 1:
Graph each inequality.
1A) $y > 3x - 5$
1B) y < x + 6

Solutions:
1A)

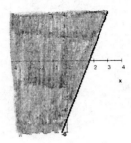

1B)

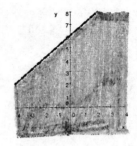

EXAMPLE 2:
Graph each inequality.

2A) $y \le -\dfrac{2}{3}x$

2B) $y \ge \dfrac{1}{5}x + 2$

Solutions:
2A)

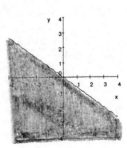

2B)

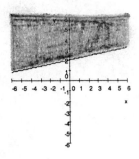

Section 7.6
EXAMPLE 1:
Which of the following relations are functions?
1A) Cost of apples: {(1, $0.25), (2, $0.50), (3, $0.75), (4,$1.00)}
1B) Appliances Owned: {(Ray, microwave), (Rich, oven), (Rich, microwave), (Ron, oven), (Ron, refrigerator), (Rick, dishwasher)}
1C) Bus Ridden: {(Terry, #1), (Thomas, #1), (A.J., #3), (Alex, #4)}
1D) {(A, 2), (B, 2), (B, 5), (C, 3)}
Solutions:
1A) Yes   **1B)** No
1C) Yes   **1D)** No

EXAMPLE 2:
2A) Assume one pound of hamburger is $1.09. Write a function to determine the cost, c, when p pounds of hamburger are purchased.
2B) Assume one adult movie ticket costs $4.50. Write a function to determine the cost, x, when t adult tickets are purchased.
Solutions:
2A) $c = 1.09p$ **2B)** $x = 4.50t$

EXAMPLE 3:
Determine whether the following sets of ordered pairs are functions:
3A) $\{(3,5),(2,4),(1,4),(-2,3)\}$
3B) $\{(3,5),(2,4),(2,3),(-2,3)\}$

3C) {(1, 5), (2, 5), (3, 5), (4, 5)}
3D) {(1, 1), (1, 2), (1, 3), (1, 5)}
Solutions:
3A) Yes   **3B)** No
3C) Yes   **3D)** No

EXAMPLE 4:
Using the vertical line test, determine whether the following graphs represent functions.
4A)

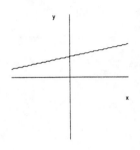

4B)

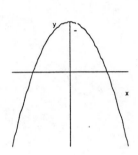

4C)

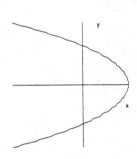

Solutions:
4A) Yes   **4B)** Yes
4C) No

EXAMPLE 5:
5A) For the function
$f(x) = x^2 - 4x + 2$, find
a) $f(2)$ and **b)** $f(-3)$. **c)** If $x = -2$, determine the value of y.
5B) For the function
$f(x) = -x^2 + 2x - 3$, find **a)** f(1) and **b)** f(-3). **c)** If x = -4, find the value of y.
Solutions:
5A) a) –2; **b)** 23; **c)** 14
5B) a) –2; **b)** –18; **c)** -27

EXAMPLE 6:
6A) Graph $f(x) = 3x + 5$.
6B) Graph $f(x) = \dfrac{2}{5}x - 3$

Solutions:
6A)

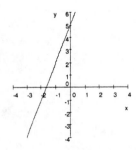

6B)

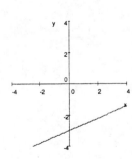

EXAMPLE 7:
7A) The weekly profit, p, of a movie theater is a function of the number of tickets sold per week, t. The function approximating the profit is $p = f(t) = 6t - 500$, where $0 \leq t \leq 1000$. **a)** Construct a graph showing the relationship between the number of ticket-buyers and the weekly profit. **b)** Estimate the profit if there are 600 tickets sold in a given week.

7B) The weekly wage, W, earned by an employee of Hardware Mart is a function of the number of hours worked per week, h. The function approximating the wage is $W = f(h) = 8h - 25$, where $0 \leq h \leq 60$. **a)** Construct a graph showing the relationship between the number of hours worked and the weekly wage. **b)** Estimate the weekly wage if a person works 45 hours in a given week.

Solutions:

7A)

a)

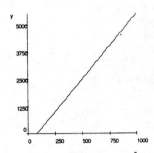

b) $3,100

7B)

a)

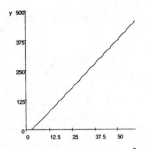

b) $335

Chapter 7: Graphing Linear Equations

Section 7.1
EXAMPLE 1:
Plot each point on the same axis.
1A) J(3, 5)   **1B)** K(5, 3)
1C) L(-2, 5)   **1D)** M(3, 0)
1E) N(-1, -3)   **1F)** P(0, -2)

1G) Q(0, 5)   **1H)** R$\left(2, \frac{5}{2}\right)$

1I) T$\left(\frac{7}{2}, -\frac{3}{2}\right)$

Solutions:

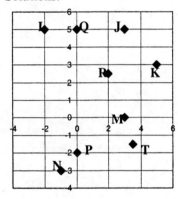

EXAMPLE 2:
List the ordered pairs for each
point shown in the figure below.

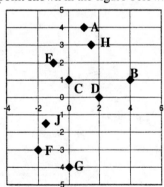

Solutions:
A(1, 4)   B(4, 1)
C(0, 1)   D(2, 0)
E(-1, 2)   F(-2, -3)

G(0, -4)   H$\left(\frac{3}{2}, 3\right)$

J$\left(-\frac{3}{2}, -\frac{3}{2}\right)$

EXAMPLE 3:
Determine whether the three
points given appear to be
collinear.
3A) (0, 4), (1.5, 0), (-3, -2)
3B) (7, 3), (3, 8), (9, 0.5)
3C) (-8, 5), (0, 10), (5, 15)
Solutions:
3A) No   **3B)** Yes
3C) Yes

EXAMPLE 4:
4A) a) Determine which of the
following ordered pairs satisfy
the equation $3x + 4y = 14$.
(3, 4), (2, 2), (-2, 5), (0, 6)
b) Plot all the points that satisfy
the equation on the same axis,
and draw a straight line through
the points. **c)** What does this
straight line represent?
4B) a) Determine which of the
following ordered pairs satisfy
the equation $-3x - 5y = -13$.
(1, 2), (-1, -2), (6, -1), (0, 3)
b) Plot all the points that satisfy
the equation on the same axis,
and draw a straight line through
the points. **c)** What does this
straight line represent?
Solutions:
4A) a) (2, 2) and (-2, 5);
b)

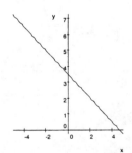

c) All of the solutions to the
equation $3x + 4y = 14$.
4B) a) (1, 2) and (6, -1);

b)

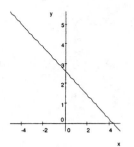

c) All of the solutions to the
equation $-3x - 5y = -13$.

Section 7.2
EXAMPLE 1:
Graph each equation.
1A) $y = 4x + 2$ **1B)** $y = 3x - 9$
Solutions:
1A)

1B)

EXAMPLE 2:
Graph each equation.
2A) $3y = 6x - 15$
2B) $2y = -3x - 18$
Solutions:
2A)

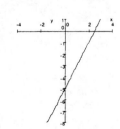

2B)

4B)

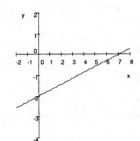

6B)

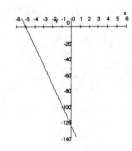

EXAMPLE 3:
Graph each equation.
3A) $3x + 7y = 0$
3B) $8x + 3y = 0$
Solutions:
3A)

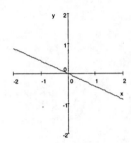

EXAMPLE 5:
Graph each equation by finding
the x- and y-intercepts.
5A) $3x + 2y = 8$
5B) $3x - 5y = 12$
Solutions:
5A)

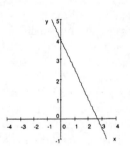

EXAMPLE 7:
Graph each equation.
7A) $y = 8$.　　　**7B)** $y = -3$.
Solutions:
7A)

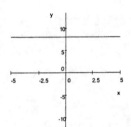

3B)

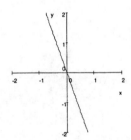

5B)

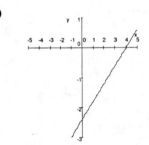

7B)

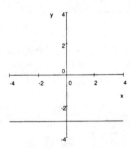

EXAMPLE 4:
Graph each equation by plotting
the x- and y-intercepts.
4A) $4y = 8x + 16$
4B) $7y = 2x - 14$
Solutions:
4A)

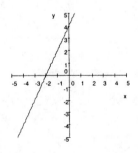

EXAMPLE 6:
Graph each equation.
6A) $y = 30x + 90$
6B) $y = -25x - 125$
Solutions:
6A)

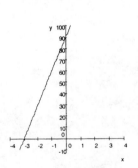

EXAMPLE 8:
Graph each equation.
8A) $x = -3$　　　**8B)** $x = 10$
Solutions:
8A)

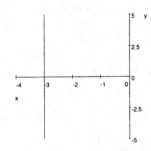

8B)

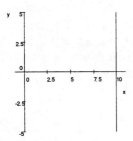

EXAMPLE 9:

9A) John Smith recently accepted a position as a sales representative at an electronics store. He is paid a bi-weekly salary plus commission on sales. He will receive a salary of $400 every two weeks plus 6% commission on all sales, s.
a) Write an equation for the salary, R, John will receive, in terms of the sales, s. **b)** Graph the salary for sales from $0 up to and including $15,000. **c)** From the graph, estimate the salary if John's bi-weekly sales are $10,000. **d)** From the graph, estimate the sales needed for John to earn a bi-weekly salary of $2000.
9B) The cost of playing at the Crestline Golf Club is a $500 yearly membership fee plus $25 green fees every time the member plays golf. **a)** Write an equation for the cost, C, that a member will pay, in terms of the number of times the member plays golf, n. **b)** Graph the cost for playing n rounds from 0 to 100. **c)** From the graph, estimate the cost to a member if he plays 25 rounds of golf. **d)** If a member spends $2300.
Solutions:
9A) a) R = 400 + 0.06s;

b)

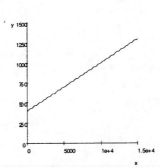

c) $1,000; **d)** Approximately $26,667
9B) a) C = 500 + 25n;
b)

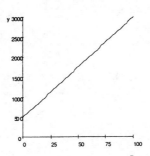

c) $1125; **d)** 72 rounds

Section 7.3

EXAMPLE 1:
1A) Find the slope of the line through the points (-2, -4) and (4, 7).
1B) Find the slope of the line through the points (3, 10) and (-3, -2).
Solutions:

1A) $\dfrac{11}{6}$ **1B)** 2

EXAMPLE 2:
2A) a) Plot the points (-3, -1) and (-1, 2) and draw a line through these points. Find the slope of the line by observing the vertical change and horizontal change between these points. **b)** Calculate the slope of the line using the two given points.

2B) a) Plot the points (1, 3) and (-1, 6) and draw a line through these points. Find the slope of the line by observing the vertical change and horizontal change between these points. **b)** Calculate the slope of the line using the two given points.
Solutions:
2A)
a)

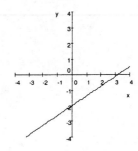

b) $m = \dfrac{3}{2}$

2B)
a)

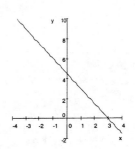

b) $m = -\dfrac{3}{2}$

EXAMPLE 3:
3A) Plot the points (-3, 1) and (2, 11) and draw a line through these points. Find the slope of the line by observing the vertical change and horizontal change between these points.
3B) Plot the points (2, 7) and (-5, 7) and draw a line through these points. Find the slope of the line by observing the vertical change and horizontal change between these points.

Solutions:
3A)
a)

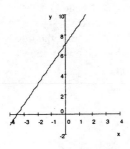

b) $m = 2$
3B)
a)

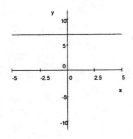

b) $m = 0$

EXAMPLE 4:
4A) Refer to Example 4 on page 466 of your text. Use the points (1994, 279) and (2000, 290) to find the slope of the red line.
4B) Refer to Exercise 71 on page 472 of your text. Use the points (55, 81) and (7, 85) to find the slope of the line connecting these points.
Solutions:

4A) $m = \dfrac{7}{2}$ **4B)** $m = -\dfrac{1}{16}$

EXAMPLE 5:
5A) a) Draw a line with a slope of $\dfrac{2}{3}$ through the point (0, -2).
b) On the same set of axis, draw a line with a slope of $\dfrac{2}{3}$ through the point (-3, 6). **c)** Are the two lines in part a) and b) parallel? Explain.

5B) a) Draw a line with a slope of 5 through the point (-3, 2).
b) On the same set of axis, draw a line with a slope of $-\dfrac{1}{5}$ through the point (3, 0). **c)** Are the two lines in part a) and b) parallel? Explain.
Solutions:
5A)
a,b)

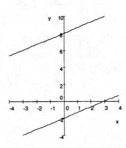

c) Yes, they have the same slopes.
5B)
a,b)

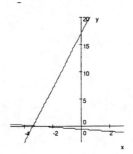

c) No, they do not have the same slopes.

EXAMPLE 6:
6A) a) Draw a line with a slope of 5 through the point (-1, -2).
b) On the same set of axis, draw a line with a slope of $-\dfrac{1}{5}$ through the point (0, 2).
c) Are the two lines in parts a) and b) perpendicular? Explain.
6B) a) Draw a line with a slope of $\dfrac{2}{3}$ through the point (0, 4).

b) On the same set of axis, draw a line with a slope of $-\dfrac{2}{3}$ through the point (0, 2).
c) Are the two lines in parts a) and b) perpendicular? Explain.
Solutions:
6A)
a,b)

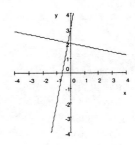

c) Yes, their slopes are negative reciprocals.
6B)
a,b)

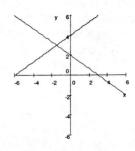

c) No, their slopes are not negative reciprocals.

EXAMPLE 7:
If m_1 represents the slope of line 1 and m_2 represents the slope of line 2, determine if line 1 and 2 are parallel, perpendicular, or neither.

7A) $m_1 = \dfrac{2}{3}$ and $m_2 = \dfrac{3}{2}$

7B) $m_1 = -3$ and $m_2 = \dfrac{1}{3}$

7C) $m_1 = \dfrac{3}{4}$ and $m_2 = \dfrac{3}{4}$

7D) $m_1 = 0.3$ and $m_2 = \dfrac{1}{3}$

7E) $m_1 = \frac{5}{8}$ and $m_2 = 0.625$

7F) $m_1 = -\frac{2}{3}$ and $m_2 = \frac{6}{4}$

Solutions:
7A) Neither
7B) Perpendicular
7C) Parallel
7D) Neither
7E) Parallel
7F) Perpendicular

Section 7.4

EXAMPLE 1:
Write each equation in slope-intercept form. State the slope and y-intercept.
1A) $-4x + 5y = 8$
1B) $9x - 6y = 12$
Solutions:

1A) $y = \frac{4}{5}x + \frac{8}{5}$; slope = $\frac{4}{5}$;

y-intercept = $\frac{8}{5}$

1B) $y = \frac{3}{2}x - 2$; slope = $\frac{3}{2}$;

y-intercept = -2

EXAMPLE 2:
Determine whether the two equations represent lines that are parallel, perpendicular, or neither.
2A) $3x + 2y = 5$ and $-6x = 4y - 10$

2B) $y = \frac{3}{5}x - 2$ and

$5x + 3y = 3$

2C) $y = \frac{2}{7}x - 5$ and

$2x + 6y = 10$

2D $2x + 6y = 9$ and

$12x + 4y = 10$

Solutions:
2A) Parallel
2B) Perpendicular
2C) Neither
2D) Neither

EXAMPLE 3:
Write each equation in slope-intercept form; then use the slope and y-intercept to graph each equation.
3A) $-4x + 7y = 14$
3B) $5x - 8y = 16$
Solutions:

3A) $y = \frac{4}{7}x + 2$

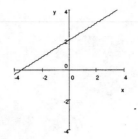

3B) $y = \frac{5}{8}x - 2$

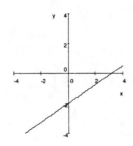

EXAMPLE 4:
Graph each equation by using the slope and y-intercept.
4A) $3x + 5y = 10$
4B) $-4x - 2y = 12$
Solutions:
4A)

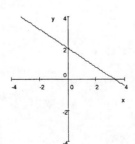

4B)

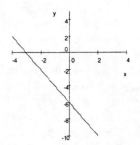

EXAMPLE 5:
Determine the equation of each of the lines shown.
5A)

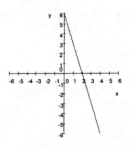

5B)

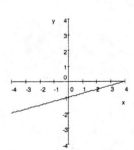

Solutions:
5A) $y = -3x + 6$

5B) $y = -\frac{1}{4}x - 1$

EXAMPLE 6:
6A) Gena Palmari bakes different types of breads and sells them out of her home. Each loaf costs $4.00. Her set cost per month of running her business averages to $100. **a)** Find the equation of the total monthly profit, P, when n loafs

are sold. **b)** Use the equation found in part a) to find the total monthly profit if 50 loafs are sold. **c)** Graph the equation in part a) and use it to check your answer in part b).

6B) On a trip across the country, Allison Murphy decides that she will keep track of her total distance traveled. She decides this after she has already traveled 300 miles. She figures that she will average a speed of 60 mph during the rest of her trip. **a)** Write an equation for the distance, D, in terms of the time, t, in hours, that describes Allison's trip. **b)** Use the equation found in part a) to find the total distance traveled if Allison drives for 12 hours (after driving the initial 300 miles). **c)** Graph the equation in part a) and use it to check your answer in part b).

Solutions:
6A) a) P = 4n - 100; **b)** $100
6B) a) D = 300 + 60t; **b)** 1020 miles

EXAMPLE 7:
Write an equation, in slope-intercept form, of the line that goes through the given point and has the given slope.
7A) (4, 2) and 6
7B) (-2, -1) and −1
Solutions:
1A) y = 6x − 22   **1B)** y = -x − 3

EXAMPLE 8:
Write an equation, in slope-intercept form, of the line that goes through the given point and has the given slope.

8A) (-4, 2) and $3/2$

8B) (1, 6) and $-1/4$

Solutions:

8A) $y = \dfrac{3}{2}x + 8$

8B) $y = -\dfrac{1}{4}x + \dfrac{25}{4}$

EXAMPLE 9:
Find an equation of the line through the given points. Write the equation in slope-intercept form.
9A) (-2, -5) and (2, 1)
9B) (3, 6) and (2, 3)
Solutions:

9A) $y = \dfrac{3}{2}x - 2$ **9B)** $y = 3x - 3$

EXAMPLE 10:
Graph each equation **a)** by plotting points; **b)** using the x- and y-intercepts; and **c)** using the slope and y-intercept.
10A) 4x − 2y = 16
10B) −6x − 3y = 15
Solutions:
10A)

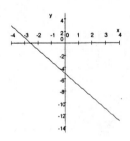

10B)

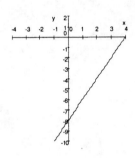

Section 7.5
EXAMPLE 1:
Graph each inequality.
1A) $y > 3x - 5$
1B) y < x + 6

Solutions:
1A)

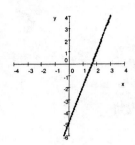

1B)

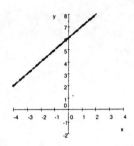

EXAMPLE 2:
Graph each inequality.

2A) $y \le -\dfrac{2}{3}x$

2B) $y \ge \dfrac{1}{5}x + 2$

Solutions:
2A)

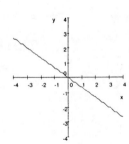

2B)

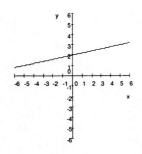

Section 7.6

EXAMPLE 1:
Which of the following relations are functions?
1A) Cost of apples: {(1, $0.25), (2, $0.50), (3, $0.75), (4,$1.00)}
1B) Appliances Owned: {(Ray, microwave), (Rich, oven), (Rich, microwave), (Ron, oven), (Ron, refrigerator), (Rick, dishwasher)}
1C) Bus Ridden: {(Terry, #1), (Thomas, #1), (A.J., #3), (Alex, #4)}
1D) {(A, 2), (B, 2), (B, 5), (C, 3)}
Solutions:
1A) Yes   **1B)** No
1C) Yes   **1D)** No

EXAMPLE 2:
2A) Assume one pound of hamburger is $1.09. Write a function to determine the cost, c, when p pounds of hamburger are purchased.
2B) Assume one adult movie ticket costs $4.50. Write a function to determine the cost, x, when t adult tickets are purchased.
Solutions:
2A) $c = 1.09p$ **2B)** $x = 4.50t$

EXAMPLE 3:
Determine whether the following sets of ordered pairs are functions:
3A) $\{(3,5),(2,4),(1,4),(-2,3)\}$
3B) $\{(3,5),(2,4),(2,3),(-2,3)\}$

3C) {(1, 5), (2, 5), (3, 5), (4, 5)}
3D) {(1, 1), (1, 2), (1, 3), (1, 5)}
Solutions:
3A) Yes   **3B)** No
3C) Yes   **3D)** No

EXAMPLE 4:
Using the vertical line test, determine whether the following graphs represent functions.
4A)

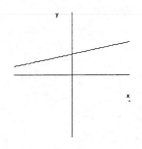

4B)

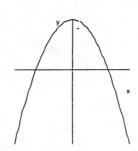

4C)

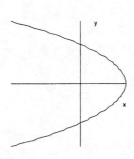

Solutions:
4A) Yes   **4B)** Yes
4C) No

EXAMPLE 5:
5A) For the function
$f(x) = x^2 - 4x + 2$, find
a) $f(2)$ and **b)** $f(-3)$. **c)** If
$x = -2$, determine the value of y.
5B) For the function
$f(x) = -x^2 + 2x - 3$, find **a)** f(1) and **b)** f(-3). **c)** If x = -4, find the value of y.
Solutions:
5A) a) –2; **b)** 23; **c)** 14
5B) a) –2; **b)** –18; **c)** -27

EXAMPLE 6:
6A) Graph $f(x) = 3x + 5$.
6B) Graph $f(x) = \dfrac{2}{5}x - 3$

Solutions:
6A)

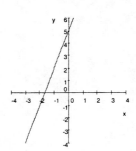

6B)

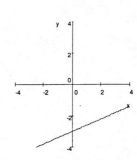

EXAMPLE 7:

7A) The weekly profit, p, of a movie theater is a function of the number of tickets sold per week, t. The function approximating the profit is $p = f(t) = 6t - 500$, where $0 \le t \le 1000$. **a)** Construct a graph showing the relationship between the number of ticket-buyers and the weekly profit. **b)** Estimate the profit if there are 600 tickets sold in a given week.

7B) The weekly wage, W, earned by an employee of Hardware Mart is a function of the number of hours worked per week, h. The function approximating the wage is $W = f(h) = 8h - 25$, where $0 \le h \le 60$. **a)** Construct a graph showing the relationship between the number of hours worked and the weekly wage. **b)** Estimate the weekly wage if a person works 45 hours in a given week.

Solutions:

7A)

a)

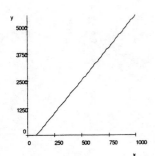

b) $3,100

7B)

a)

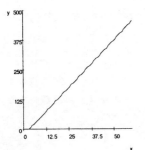

b) $335

Chapter 8: Systems of Linear Equations

Section 8.1
EXAMPLE 1:
For each system of equations, determine which of the given ordered pairs satisfy the system of equations.

1A) (2, 1) and (-1, 13)
$$\begin{cases} y = 4x - 9 \\ 8x + 2y = 18 \end{cases}$$

1B) (4, 9) and (3, 7)
$$\begin{cases} 2x - y = -1 \\ -4x + 5y = 23 \end{cases}$$

Solutions:
1A) Yes; No   **1B)** No; Yes

EXAMPLE 2:
Determine whether each system has exactly one solution, no solution, or an infinite number of solutions.

2A)
$$\begin{cases} 2x + 4y = 9 \\ 4x + 8y = 18 \end{cases}$$

2B)
$$\begin{cases} x + 3y = 5 \\ 2x + 5y = -10 \end{cases}$$

2C)
$$\begin{cases} x + 3y = 5 \\ 2x + 6y = 7 \end{cases}$$

Solutions:
2A) An infinite number of solutions
2B) One solution
2C) No solutions

EXAMPLE 3:
Solve each system of equations graphically.

3A)
$$\begin{cases} 3x + y = 9 \\ x + 4y = 14 \end{cases}$$

3B)
$$\begin{cases} -x + y = 3 \\ x + y = 7 \end{cases}$$

Solutions:
3A) (2, 3)   **3B)** (2, 5)

EXAMPLE 4:
Solve each system of equations graphically.

4A)
$$\begin{cases} 2x + y = 5 \\ 5x + 2y = 10 \end{cases}$$

4B)
$$\begin{cases} -x + y = 6 \\ 5x - 2y = -9 \end{cases}$$

Solutions:
4A) (0, 5)   **4B)** (1, 7)

EXAMPLE 5:
Solve each system of equations graphically.

5A)
$$\begin{cases} x - \dfrac{2}{3}y = 6 \\ y = 3x - 6 \end{cases}$$

5B)
$$\begin{cases} \dfrac{1}{2}x + y = 7 \\ 3y = 2x - 7 \end{cases}$$

Solutions:
5A) (-2, -12)   **5B)** (8, 3)

EXAMPLE 6:
6A) Timothy is considering buying a new air conditioner. His current air conditioner is in need of repair; this repair would cost $650. A new air conditioner will cost $2100. The cost of operating the old air conditioner is $800 per year. The estimated cost of operating the new air conditioner is $600. Find the number of years for which the total cost of repair would equal the total cost of replacement.

6B) Lisa would like to hire a landscaping service to work on her yard. Greentree Landscaping Company charges a consultation fee of $275 plus $45 per hour for labor. Happy Valley Landscaping Service charges a consultation fee of $350 plus $30 per hour for labor. Find the number of hours of labor for the two services to have the same cost.

Solutions:
6A) 7.25 years   **6B)** 5 hours

Section 8.2
EXAMPLE 1:
Solve each system of equations by substitution.

1A)
$$\begin{cases} 3x + y = 13 \\ 2x + 2y = 14 \end{cases}$$

1B)
$$\begin{cases} 2x + y = 1 \\ 2x + 5y = -3 \end{cases}$$

Solutions:
1A) (3, 4)   **1B)** (1, -1)

EXAMPLE 2:
Solve each system of equations by substitution.

2A)
$$\begin{cases} 2x + y = 1 \\ 6x - 3y = 10 \end{cases}$$

2B)
$$\begin{cases} 2x - y = 10 \\ -x + \dfrac{1}{2}y = 3 \end{cases}$$

Solutions:
2A) No solution
2B) No solution

EXAMPLE 3:
Solve each system of equations by substitution.

3A)
$$\begin{cases} 2x + y = 1 \\ 6x + 3y = 3 \end{cases}$$

3B)
$$\begin{cases} -x - y = -8 \\ 4x + 4y = 32 \end{cases}$$

Solutions:
3A) An infinite number of solutions.
3B) An infinite number of solutions.

EXAMPLE 4:
Solve each system of equations by substitution.

4A)
$$\begin{cases} 5x - y = 4 \\ x + \dfrac{1}{2}y = -2 \end{cases}$$

4B) $\begin{cases} 7x + y = 12 \\ x - 2y = -9 \end{cases}$

Solutions:
4A) (0, -4)   **4B)** (1, 5)

EXAMPLE 5:
Solve each system of equations by substitution.

5A) $\begin{cases} x = 2y - 2 \\ -2x + y = -5 \end{cases}$

5B) $\begin{cases} y = -x + 3 \\ -x - y = -3 \end{cases}$

Solutions:
5A) (4, 3)   **5B)** (-2, 5)

EXAMPLE 6:
6A) In 2001 and 2002, a total of 10,872 tickets were sold at the Cinema 9 movie theater. If the number of tickets sold in 2002 is 158 more than the number sold in 2001, find the number of tickets sold in 2001 and 2002.
6B) Jonas is an insurance salesman. During 2001 and 2002, he met with a total of 284 different people. The number of people he met with in 2001 is 24 less than the number of people he met with in 2002. Find the number of people Jonas met with in 2001 and 2002.
Solutions:
6A) 5,357 tickets in 2001 and 5,515 tickets in 2002
6B) 130 people in 2001 and 154 people in 2002

Section 8.3
EXAMPLE 1:
Solve each system of equations using the addition method

1A) $\begin{cases} 2x + 3y = 9 \\ x + y = 3 \end{cases}$

1B) $\begin{cases} x + y = 5 \\ 2x - y = -11 \end{cases}$

Solutions:
1A) (0, 3)   **1B)** (-2, 7)

EXAMPLE 2:
Solve each system of equations using the addition method.

2A) $\begin{cases} x + 2y = 5 \\ x + 3y = 7 \end{cases}$

2B) $\begin{cases} 5x + y = -5 \\ 6x + y = -6 \end{cases}$

Solutions:
2A) (1, 2)   **2B)** (-1, 0)

EXAMPLE 3:
Solve each system of equations using the addition method.

3A) $\begin{cases} 5x + y = -3 \\ x + 3y = 5 \end{cases}$

3B) $\begin{cases} x + 2y = 2 \\ 3x + y = 16 \end{cases}$

Solutions:
3A) (-1, 2)   **3B)** (6, -2)

EXAMPLE 4:
Solve each system of equations using the addition method.

4A) $\begin{cases} 5x - 3y = 1 \\ 3x + y = 2 \end{cases}$

4B) $\begin{cases} x + 2y = 2 \\ 3x + 3y = 5 \end{cases}$

Solutions:
4A) $\left(\dfrac{1}{2}, \dfrac{1}{2} \right)$ **4B)** $\left(\dfrac{4}{3}, \dfrac{1}{3} \right)$

EXAMPLE 5:
Solve each system of equations using the addition method.

5A) $\begin{cases} 3x + 2y = -10 \\ 5x - 3y = -4 \end{cases}$

5B) $\begin{cases} -6x + 5y = -11 \\ 4x - 3y = 7 \end{cases}$

Solutions:
5A) (-2, -2)   **5B)** (1, -1)

EXAMPLE 6:
Solve each system of equations using the addition method.

6A) $\begin{cases} 3x + y = 12 \\ 9x + 3y = 13 \end{cases}$

6B) $\begin{cases} x - y = 2 \\ -3x + 3y = 7 \end{cases}$

Solutions:
6A) No solution
6B) No solution

EXAMPLE 7:
Solve each system of equations using the addition method.

7A) $\begin{cases} 5x - 2y = 3 \\ 10x - 4y = 6 \end{cases}$

7B) $\begin{cases} 7x + 12y = 4 \\ \dfrac{7}{2}x + 6y = 2 \end{cases}$

Solutions:
7A) An infinite number of solutions.
7B) An infinite number of solutions.

EXAMPLE 8:
Solve each system of equations using the addition method.

8A) $\begin{cases} 7x + 6y = 13 \\ 8x + 5y = 12 \end{cases}$

8B) $\begin{cases} 8x + 16y = 13 \\ -12x - 20y = -17 \end{cases}$

Solutions:
8A) $\left(\dfrac{7}{13}, \dfrac{20}{13} \right)$ **8B)** $\left(\dfrac{3}{8}, \dfrac{5}{8} \right)$

Section 8.4
EXAMPLE 1:
1A) Marianne wants to build a rectangular fence around her garden. When she measures the two angles formed by a diagonal, she finds that one angle is 20° more than the other angle. Find the two angles.
1B) In any right triangle, the non-right (acute) angles are complementary. In a certain right triangle, one acute angle is 12° more than the other acute angle. Find the two angles.
Solutions:
1A) 35°, 55°   **1B)** 39°, 51°

EXAMPLE 2:
2A) The perimeter of Greg's rectangular deck is 170 feet. The length of the deck is 4 times its width. Find the dimensions of the deck.
2B) The perimeter of a parallelogram-shaped slab of concrete is 24 feet. The width of the slab is half the length of its length. Find the dimensions of the slab.
Solutions:
2A) 17 x 68 feet **2B)** 4 x 8 feet

EXAMPLE 3:
3A) Tickets to the Wayne Valley Basketball game last Friday were $5.00 for adults and $3.00 for children. There were a total of 300 tickets sold, and the total ticket sales were $1310. Find the number of each type of ticket sold.
3B) The Sterling Boys Club took a group trip to Worlds of Fun in Kansas City, MO. A total of 34 people went on the trip, including several adults. Tickets to the park were $35 for adults and $20 for children under 18 years old. If the total costs of the groups' tickets were $770, find the number of children and adults in the group.
Solutions:
3A) 95 children tickets and 205 adult tickets
3B) 6 adults and 28 children

EXAMPLE 4:
4A) Tony and Sharon's house needs painted, and they would like to hire someone to do the job. The Paint Store charges a fee of $400 plus $20 per hour for labor. Sunshine Painting Service charges a $275 fee plus $25 per hour for labor. **a)** How long does it take for the cost of the painting services to be the same? **b)** If both services estimate the time required to finish the job to be 32 hours, which service would be less expensive?

4B) The Jones Bar-B-Que Pit offers a full-slab meal for $15.95 per person. However, they are running a promotional special in which customers buy a "Jones Card" for $15 and then are entitled to 8 full-slab meals for $10.95 per person. **a)** After how many full-slab meals, using the "Jones Card" with each meal, would the amount the customer saves equal the cost of the Card? **b)** If a customer bought and used 3 "Jones Cards" in one year, how much would they save?
Solutions:
4A) a) 25 hours; **b)** The Paint Store would be less expensive
4B) a) After 3 full-slab meals; **b)** $75

EXAMPLE 5:
5A) Sally and Rhonda live in towns that are 30 miles apart. Occasionally they will ride their bikes and meet somewhere in the middle. Then they will continue their ride throughout the day. On one particular day, Sally and Rhonda leave at the same time. They meet each other 2 hours after they began. Find Sally and Rhonda's speed if Sally rides an average speed of 2 miles per hours faster than Rhonda.
5B) Thomas Miller and his family are taking their motorboat on a roundtrip up and down the river. They will be traveling 21 miles upstream and 21 miles downstream. The trip upstream takes 1.75 hours, while the trip downstream takes 1.5 hours. Determine the speed of the current.
Solutions:
5A) Sally's speed is 8.5 mph; Rhonda's speed is 6.5 mph
5B) The speed of the current is 1 mile per hour

EXAMPLE 6:
6A) At the Nut Shop, a customer requests 10 pounds of a mixture of cashews and peanuts. The cashews are $6.50 per pound, and the peanuts are $3.50 per pound. If the mixture costs $44, how much of each type of nut is in the mixture?
6B) At the Confectioner's Corner, a local candy store, a customer requests a mixture of different types of candies. The customer wants butterscotch candies and mint melt-a-ways in the mixture. The butterscotch candies cost $2.75 per pound and the mint melt-a-ways cost $4.25 per pound. The customer buys 6 pounds of the mixture. The cost of the mixture is $21.75, how much of each type of candy is in the mixture?
Solutions:
6A) Seven pounds of peanuts and 3 pounds of cashews
6B) 2.5 pounds of the butterscotch candies and 3.5 pounds of the mint melt-a-ways

EXAMPLE 7:
7A) A chemist needs a 20% solution of sulfuric acid. He has an ample supply of both 10% and 25% sulfuric acid solutions. If he wants to make 50 liters of a 20% sulfuric acid solution, how many liters of the 10% and 25% solution should he mix?
7B) A chemist needs a 50% alcohol solution. She has supplies of both 40% and 70% alcohol solutions. How much of each type of alcohol solution should be mixed to make 10 liters of a 50% alcohol solution?
Solutions:
7A) $33\frac{1}{3}$ Liters of the 25% solution, and $16\frac{2}{3}$ liters of the 10% solution
7B) $3\frac{1}{3}$ liters of the 70% solution and $6\frac{2}{3}$ liters of the 40% solution.

Section 8.5

EXAMPLE 1:

Determine the solutions to the following system of inequalities.

1A) $\begin{cases} x + 3y < 9 \\ y \geq 2x - 5 \end{cases}$

1B) $\begin{cases} x - y \leq 4 \\ y > x + 3 \end{cases}$

Solutions:

1A)

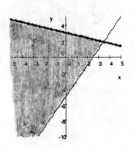

1B)

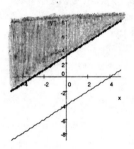

EXAMPLE 2:

Determine the solution to the following system of inequalities.

2A) $\begin{cases} 2x + 4y > 8 \\ 2x - y \geq -2 \end{cases}$

2B) $\begin{cases} x - 3y < -4 \\ x + 2y \leq 6 \end{cases}$

Solutions:

2A)

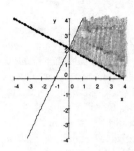

2B)

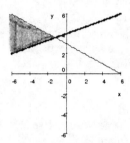

EXAMPLE 3:

Determine the solution to the following system of inequalities.

3A) $\begin{cases} y < -4 \\ x > 6 \end{cases}$ 3B) $\begin{cases} x \geq 2 \\ y \leq -1 \end{cases}$

Solutions:

3A)

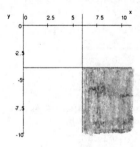

3B)

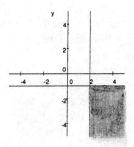

Chapter 9: Roots and Radicals

Section 9.1

EXAMPLE 1:
Evaluate.

1A) $\sqrt{225}$ **1B)** $\sqrt{400}$
Solutions:
1A) 15   **1B)** 20

EXAMPLE 2:
Evaluate.

2A) $-\sqrt{225}$ **2B)** $-\sqrt{400}$
Solutions:
2A) -15 **2B)** -20

EXAMPLE 3:
Indicate whether the radical expression is a real number of an imaginary number.

3A) $-\sqrt{25}$ **3B)** $\sqrt{-25}$
3C) $\sqrt{-41}$ **3D)** $-\sqrt{41}$
Solutions:
3A) Real (equal to -5)
3B) Imaginary
3C) Imaginary
3D) Real

EXAMPLE 4:
Use your calculator or Table 9.1 to determine whether the following square roots are rational or irrational numbers.

4A) $\sqrt{625}$ **4B)** $\sqrt{160}$
4C) $\sqrt{121}$ **4D)** $\sqrt{636}$
Solutions:
4A) Rational, equal to 25
4B) Irrational
4C) Rational, equal to 11
4D) Irrational

EXAMPLE 5:
Write each radical expression in exponential form.

5A) $\sqrt{7}$ **5B)** $\sqrt{15y}$
5C) $\sqrt{45x^2 y}$ **5D)** $\sqrt{20x^3}$
Solutions:
5A) $7^{1/2}$ **5B)** $(15y)^{1/2}$
5C) $(45x^2 y)^{1/2}$ **5D)** $(20x^3)^{1/2}$

Section 9.2

EXAMPLE 1:
Simplify

1A) $\sqrt{120}$ **1B)** $\sqrt{63}$
Solutions:
1A) $2\sqrt{30}$ **1B)** $3\sqrt{7}$

EXAMPLE 2:
Simplify

2A) $\sqrt{75}$ **2B)** $\sqrt{24}$
Solutions:
2A) $5\sqrt{3}$ **2B)** $2\sqrt{6}$

EXAMPLE 3:
Simplify

3A) $\sqrt{108}$ **3B)** $\sqrt{98}$
Solutions:
3A) $6\sqrt{3}$ **3B)** $7\sqrt{2}$

EXAMPLE 4:
Simplify

4A) $\sqrt{125}$ **4B)** $\sqrt{192}$
Solutions:
4A) $5\sqrt{5}$ **4B)** $8\sqrt{3}$

EXAMPLE 5:
Simplify

5A) $\sqrt{92}$ **5B)** $\sqrt{99}$
Solutions:
5A) $2\sqrt{23}$ **5B)** $3\sqrt{11}$

EXAMPLE 6:
Simplify

6A) $\sqrt{x^{40}}$ **6B)** $\sqrt{x^{10} y^{12}}$
6C) $\sqrt{m^4 n^{18}}$ **6D)** $\sqrt{w^{20} x^2}$
Solutions:
6A) x^{20} **6B)** $x^5 y^6$
6C) $m^2 n^9$ **6D)** $w^{10} x$

EXAMPLE 7:
Simplify

7A) $\sqrt{x^7}$ **7B)** $\sqrt{y^{13}}$
7C) $\sqrt{m^{35}}$ **7D)** $\sqrt{w^{73}}$
Solutions:
7A) $x^3 \sqrt{x}$ **7B)** $y^6 \sqrt{y}$
7C) $m^{17} \sqrt{m}$ **7D)** $w^{36} \sqrt{w}$

EXAMPLE 8:
Simplify

8A) $\sqrt{16y^3}$ **8B)** $\sqrt{36w^5}$
8C) $\sqrt{72x^2}$ **8D)** $\sqrt{72x^4}$
8E) $\sqrt{72x^5}$ **8F)** $\sqrt{72x^3}$
Solutions:
8A) $4y\sqrt{y}$ **8B)** $6w^2 \sqrt{w}$
8C) $6x\sqrt{2}$ **8D)** $6x^2 \sqrt{2}$
8E) $6x^2 \sqrt{2x}$ **8F)** $6x\sqrt{2x}$

EXAMPLE 9:
Simplify

9A) $\sqrt{72xy^2}$ **9B)** $\sqrt{72x^4 y}$
9C) $\sqrt{18x^4 y}$ **9D)** $\sqrt{18x^3 y^4}$
9E) $\sqrt{12x^7 y^8}$ **9F)** $\sqrt{12x^{10} y^8}$
Solutions:
9A) $6y\sqrt{2x}$ **9B)** $6x^2 \sqrt{2y}$
9C) $3x^2 \sqrt{2y}$ **9D)** $3xy^2 \sqrt{2x}$
9E) $2x^3 y^4 \sqrt{3x}$ **9F)** $2x^5 y^4 \sqrt{3}$

EXAMPLE 10:
Multiply and then simplify.

10A) $\sqrt{3} \bullet \sqrt{27}$
10B) $\sqrt{5} \bullet \sqrt{125}$
10C) $\sqrt{3x} \bullet \sqrt{27}$
10D) $\sqrt{5x} \bullet \sqrt{125}$
10E) $\left(\sqrt{2x}\right)^2$
10F) $\left(\sqrt{5x}\right)^2$
Solutions:
10A) 9   **10B)** 25
10C) $9\sqrt{x}$ **10D)** $25\sqrt{x}$
10E) $2x$ **10F)** $5x$

EXAMPLE 11:
Multiply and then simplify.

11A) $\sqrt{27m^3n} \bullet \sqrt{9mn^5}$

11B) $\sqrt{16m^2n^5} \bullet \sqrt{8m^3n^3}$

11C) $\sqrt{7xy^9} \bullet \sqrt{10x^3y^4}$

11D) $\sqrt{12xy} \bullet \sqrt{13x^5y}$

Solutions:

11A) $9m^2n^3\sqrt{3}$

11B) $8m^2n^4\sqrt{2m}$

11C) $x^2y^6\sqrt{70y}$

11D) $2x^3y\sqrt{39}$

Section 9.3
EXAMPLE 1:
Simplify if possible.

1A) $3\sqrt{3} + 5\sqrt{3} - 7$

1B) $-\sqrt{6} - 2 - 7\sqrt{6}$

1C) $-6\sqrt{5} + 20 + 17\sqrt{5}$

1D) $-6\sqrt{5} + 20 + 17$

1E) $-6\sqrt{7} + 20\sqrt{x} + \sqrt{7} - \sqrt{x}$

1F) $\sqrt{13} + \sqrt{x} - \sqrt{13} + \sqrt{x}$

Solutions:

1A) $8\sqrt{3} - 7$

1B) $-8\sqrt{6} - 2$

1C) $11\sqrt{5} + 20$

1D) $-6\sqrt{5} + 37$

1E) $-5\sqrt{7} + 19\sqrt{x}$

1F) $2\sqrt{x}$

EXAMPLE 2:
Simplify.

2A) $9\sqrt{m} + 2\sqrt{m} - 10\sqrt{m}$

2B) $-3\sqrt{n} + 5\sqrt{n} + 12\sqrt{n}$

2C) $b + \sqrt{b} - 8\sqrt{b}$

2D) $r + 3r - 7\sqrt{r}$

2E) $x + 3\sqrt{x} + 3x - 7\sqrt{x}$

2F) $\sqrt{y} + 3 + 10\sqrt{y} - y$

2G) $\sqrt{mn} + 3\sqrt{m} + 10\sqrt{mn}$

2H) $\sqrt{m} + 4\sqrt{mn} + \sqrt{nm}$

Solutions:

2A) $\sqrt{m}$

2B) $14\sqrt{n}$

2C) $b - 7\sqrt{b}$

2D) $4r - 7\sqrt{r}$

2E) $4x - 4\sqrt{x} +$

2F) $11\sqrt{y} + 3 - y$

2G) $11\sqrt{mn} + 3\sqrt{m}$

2H) $\sqrt{m} + 5\sqrt{mn}$

EXAMPLE 3:
Simplify.

3A) $\sqrt{2} + \sqrt{32}$

3B) $\sqrt{45} + \sqrt{5}$

Solutions:

3A) $5\sqrt{2}$ **3B)** $4\sqrt{3}$

EXAMPLE 4:
Simplify.

4A) $\sqrt{45} - \sqrt{20}$

4B) $\sqrt{54} - \sqrt{24}$

Solutions:

4A) $\sqrt{5}$ **4B)** $\sqrt{6}$

EXAMPLE 5:
Simplify.

5A) $3\sqrt{27} - \sqrt{243}$

5B) $\sqrt{125} - 4\sqrt{3125}$

5C) $4\sqrt{48} + 3\sqrt{12} + 9$

5D) $7\sqrt{8} + 2\sqrt{18} - 2$

5E) $9\sqrt{40} + 3\sqrt{54}$

5F) $\sqrt{60} + 2\sqrt{84}$

Solutions:

5A) $-6\sqrt{3}$

5B) $-95\sqrt{5}$

5C) $22\sqrt{3} + 9$

5D) $20\sqrt{2} - 2$

5E) $18\sqrt{10} + 9\sqrt{6}$

5F) $2\sqrt{15} + 4\sqrt{21}$

EXAMPLE 6:
Multiply.

6A) $\sqrt{2}\left(\sqrt{15} + 5\right)$

6B) $\sqrt{3}\left(7 - \sqrt{21}\right)$

6C) $\sqrt{3x}\left(\sqrt{x} + \sqrt{5y}\right)$

6D) $\sqrt{5m}\left(\sqrt{2n} - \sqrt{m}\right)$

Solutions:

6A) $\sqrt{30} + 5\sqrt{2}$

6B) $7\sqrt{3} - 3\sqrt{7}$

6C) $x\sqrt{3} + \sqrt{15xy}$

6D) $\sqrt{10mn} - m\sqrt{5}$

EXAMPLE 7:
Multiply using the FOIL method.

7A) $\left(5 + \sqrt{3}\right)\left(3 - 3\sqrt{3}\right)$

7B) $\left(10 - 2\sqrt{2}\right)\left(1 + \sqrt{2}\right)$

Solutions:

7A) $6 - 12\sqrt{3}$ **7B)** $6 + 8\sqrt{2}$

EXAMPLE 8:
Multiply using the FOIL method.

8A) $\left(\sqrt{3} - \sqrt{13}\right)\left(\sqrt{3} + \sqrt{13}\right)$

8B) $\left(\sqrt{6} + \sqrt{7}\right)\left(\sqrt{6} - \sqrt{7}\right)$

Solutions:
8A) -10 **8B)** -1

Section 9.4
EXAMPLE 1:
Simplify.

1A) $\sqrt{\dfrac{64}{8}}$ **1B)** $\sqrt{\dfrac{81}{9}}$

1C) $\sqrt{\dfrac{125}{5}}$ **1D)** $\sqrt{\dfrac{36}{9}}$

1E) $\sqrt{\dfrac{9}{4}}$ **1F)** $\sqrt{\dfrac{16}{49}}$

Solutions:

1A) $2\sqrt{2}$ **1B)** 3

1C) 5 **1D)** 2

1E) $\dfrac{3}{2}$ **1F)** $\dfrac{4}{7}$

EXAMPLE 2:
Simplify.

2A) $\sqrt{\dfrac{20y^2}{10}}$ **2B)** $\sqrt{\dfrac{30y^4}{5}}$

2C) $\sqrt{\dfrac{180ab^2}{6}}$ **2D)** $\sqrt{\dfrac{70x^2y^2}{7}}$

2E) $\sqrt{\dfrac{5a^2b^2}{125a^6}}$ **2F)** $\sqrt{\dfrac{2x^2y}{8y^3}}$

2G) $\sqrt{\dfrac{30x^2y^5z}{5xy^3z}}$

2H) $\sqrt{\dfrac{42m^4n^2p}{6m^2np^5}}$

Solutions:

2A) $y\sqrt{2}$ **2B)** $y^2\sqrt{6}$

2C) $b\sqrt{30a}$ **2D)** $xy\sqrt{10}$

2E) $\dfrac{b}{5a^2}$ **2F)** $\dfrac{x}{2y}$

2G) $y\sqrt{6x}$ **2H)** $\dfrac{m^2\sqrt{7n}}{p^2}$

EXAMPLE 3:
Simplify.

3A) $\dfrac{\sqrt{3}}{\sqrt{27}}$ **3B)** $\dfrac{\sqrt{4}}{\sqrt{64}}$

3C) $\dfrac{\sqrt{18}}{\sqrt{2}}$ **3D)** $\dfrac{\sqrt{80}}{\sqrt{5}}$

Solutions:

3A) $\dfrac{1}{3}$ **3B)** $\dfrac{1}{4}$

3C) 3   **3D)** 4

EXAMPLE 4:
Simplify.

4A) $\dfrac{\sqrt{243x^6y^3}}{\sqrt{27xy}}$ **4B)** $\dfrac{\sqrt{81a^5b^4}}{\sqrt{9ab^2}}$

4C) $\dfrac{\sqrt{32x^9y^3}}{\sqrt{2xy^7}}$ **4D)** $\dfrac{\sqrt{27m^5n}}{\sqrt{3mn^5}}$

Solutions:

4A) $3x^2y\sqrt{x}$ **4B)** $3a^2b$

4C) $\dfrac{4x^4}{y^2}$ **4D)** $\dfrac{3m^2}{n^2}$

EXAMPLE 5:
Simplify.

5A) $\dfrac{1}{\sqrt{5}}$ **5B)** $\dfrac{1}{\sqrt{n}}$

Solutions:

5A) $\dfrac{\sqrt{5}}{5}$ **5B)** $\dfrac{\sqrt{n}}{n}$

EXAMPLE 6:
Simplify.

6A) $\sqrt{\dfrac{3}{7}}$ **6B)** $\sqrt{\dfrac{13}{3}}$

6C) $\sqrt{\dfrac{x^2}{8}}$ **6D)** $\sqrt{\dfrac{a^4}{45}}$

Solutions:

6A) $\dfrac{\sqrt{21}}{7}$ **6B)** $\dfrac{\sqrt{39}}{3}$

6C) $\dfrac{x\sqrt{2}}{4}$ **6D)** $\dfrac{a^2\sqrt{5}}{15}$

EXAMPLE 7:
Simplify.

7A) $\dfrac{7}{3+\sqrt{2}}$ **7B)** $\dfrac{2}{5+\sqrt{3}}$

Solutions:

7A) $3-\sqrt{2}$ **7B)** $\dfrac{5-\sqrt{3}}{11}$

EXAMPLE 8:
Simplify.

8A) $\dfrac{3}{7-\sqrt{3}}$ **8B)** $\dfrac{7}{10-\sqrt{5}}$

Solutions:

8A) $\dfrac{7+\sqrt{3}}{23}$ **8B)** $\dfrac{70+7\sqrt{5}}{95}$

EXAMPLE 9:
Simplify.

9A) $\dfrac{\sqrt{7}}{5-\sqrt{5}}$ **9B)** $\dfrac{\sqrt{5}}{9-\sqrt{7}}$

Solutions:

9A) $\dfrac{5\sqrt{7}+\sqrt{35}}{20}$

9B) $\dfrac{9\sqrt{5}+\sqrt{35}}{74}$

EXAMPLE 10:
Simplify.

10A) $\dfrac{a}{a-\sqrt{b}}$ **10B)** $\dfrac{x}{y+\sqrt{x}}$

Solutions:

10A) $\dfrac{a^2+a\sqrt{b}}{a^2-b}$

10B) $\dfrac{x^2-y\sqrt{x}}{y^2-x}$.

Section 9.5

EXAMPLE 1:
Solve each equation.

1A) $\sqrt{x}=6$ **1B)** $\sqrt{y}=8$

Solutions:
1A) x = 36   **1B)** y = 64

EXAMPLE 2:
Solve each equation.

2A) $\sqrt{x-9}=3$

2B) $\sqrt{n-4}=12$

Solutions:
2A) x = 18   **2B)** n = 148

EXAMPLE 3:
Solve each equation.

3A) $\sqrt{x}+4=12$

3B) $\sqrt{z}-5=2$

Solutions:
3A) x = 64   **3B)** z = 49

EXAMPLE 4:
Solve each equation.

4A) $\sqrt{z}=-2$

4B) $\sqrt{p}=-20$

Solutions:
4A) No real solution
4B) No real solution

EXAMPLE 5:
Solve each equation.

5A) $\sqrt{3p-5} = p-5$

5B) $\sqrt{2x-2} = x-1$
Solutions:
5A) p = 10   **5B)** x = 1, 3

EXAMPLE 6:
Solve each equation.
6A) $x-12-4\sqrt{x} = 0$
6B) $\sqrt{x}-2x+1 = 0$
Solutions:

6A) x = 36   **6B)** x = $\dfrac{1}{4}$

EXAMPLE 7:
Solve each equation.

7A) $\sqrt{3x-2} = \sqrt{2x+5}$

7B) $\sqrt{2x+6} = \sqrt{7x+1}$
Solutions:
7A) x = 7   **7B)** x = 1

EXAMPLE 8:
Solve each equation.
8A) $3\sqrt{r+5} - \sqrt{11r-17} = 0$
8B) $\sqrt{5x+3} - 2\sqrt{x+1} = 0$
Solutions:
8A) r = 31   **8B)** x = 1

Section 9.6
EXAMPLE 1:
Find the hypotenuse of a right triangle whose legs' lengths are given.

1A) $\sqrt{5}$ and 6 inches

1B) $\sqrt{5}$ and $\sqrt{6}$ feet
Solutions:
1A) 41 inches   **1B)** 11 feet

EXAMPLE 2:
2A) A rectangular deck has a length of 15 feet and a width of 10 feet. What is the length of the diagonal of the deck?

2B) A rectangular garden has a length of 24 feet and a width of 14 feet. What is the length of the diagonal of the garden?
Solutions:
2A) Approximately 18.0 feet
2B) Approximately 27.8 feet

EXAMPLE 3:
Find the length of the line segment between the given points.
3A) (-3, -5) and (2, 6)
3B) (5, 9) and (-11, 2)
Solutions:
3A) 12.08 units
3B) 17.46 units

EXAMPLE 4:
Refer to Example 4 on page 595 of your text. Use the formula given to find S given the following information.
4A) $c = 0.70, l = 30$ feet
4B) $c = 0.73, l = 50$ feet
Solutions:
4A) $S \approx 25$ mph
4B) $S \approx 33$ mph

EXAMPLE 5:
Refer to Example 5 on page 596 of your text. Use the formula to find v given the following information.
5A) $h = 50$ feet
5B) $h = 30$ meters (use g = 9.8 meters per second squared)
Solutions:
5A) $v \approx 56.6$ feet per second
5B) $v \approx 24.2$ meters per second

EXAMPLE 6:
Refer to Example 6 on page 596 of your text. Use the formula given to find T given the following information.
6A) L=10 feet   **6B)** L=20 feet
Solutions:
6A) $T \approx 3.51$ seconds
6B) $T \approx 4.97$ seconds

Section 9.7
EXAMPLE 1:
Evaluate.

1A) $\sqrt[3]{-125}$ **1B)** $\sqrt[3]{-343}$

1C) $\sqrt[3]{125}$ **1D)** $\sqrt[3]{343}$
Solutions
1A) –5   **1B)** –7
1C) 5   **1D)** 7

EXAMPLE 2:
Simplify.

2A) $\sqrt[3]{81}$ **2B)** $\sqrt[3]{625}$

2C) $\sqrt[3]{56}$ **2D)** $\sqrt[3]{135}$

2E) $\sqrt[4]{162}$ **2F)** $\sqrt[4]{243}$
Solutions:

2A) $3\sqrt[3]{3}$ **2B)** $5\sqrt[3]{5}$

2C) $2\sqrt[3]{7}$ **2D)** $3\sqrt[3]{5}$

2E) $3\sqrt[4]{2}$ **2F)** $3\sqrt[4]{3}$

EXAMPLE 3:
Write each radical expression in radical form.

3A) $\sqrt[3]{y^7}$ **3B)** $\sqrt[5]{x^2}$

3Cc) $\sqrt[13]{a^9}$ **3D)** $\sqrt[12]{b^9}$
Solutions:

3A) $y^{\frac{7}{3}}$ **3B)** $x^{\frac{2}{5}}$

3C) $a^{\frac{9}{13}}$ **3D)** $b^{\frac{3}{4}}$

EXAMPLE 4:
Simplify.

3A) $\sqrt[4]{b^{16}}$ **3B)** $\sqrt[8]{b^{48}}$

4C) $\sqrt{x^{34}}$ **4D)** $\sqrt{x^{24}}$
Solutions:
4A) b^4 **4B)** b^6
4C) x^{17} **4D)** x^{12}

EXAMPLE 5:
Evaluate.

5A) $8^{\frac{2}{3}}$ **5B)** $125^{\frac{4}{3}}$

5C) $81^{\frac{3}{4}}$ **5D)** $16^{\frac{3}{4}}$

5E) $16^{-\frac{3}{4}}$ **5F)** $16^{-\frac{5}{2}}$

Solutions:
5A) 4   **5B)** 625
5C) 27   **5D)** 8

5E) $\dfrac{1}{8}$ **5F)** $\dfrac{1}{4^5}$

EXAMPLE 6:
Simplify.

6A) $\sqrt[4]{36^2}$ **6B)** $\sqrt[4]{81^3}$

6C) $\sqrt[3]{27^3}$ **6D)** $\sqrt[3]{8^5}$

Solutions:
6A) 6   **6B)** 27
6C) 27   **6D)** 32

EXAMPLE 7:
Simplify each expression and write the answer in radical form.

7A) $\sqrt[10]{x^5}$ **7B)** $\sqrt[15]{x^5}$

7C) $\sqrt[48]{x^{24}}$ **7D)** $\sqrt[20]{x^4}$

Solutions:
7A) $\sqrt{x}$ **7B)** $\sqrt[3]{x}$

7C) $\sqrt{x}$ **7D)** $\sqrt[5]{x}$

EXAMPLE 8:
Simplify.

8A) $\sqrt{y} \cdot \sqrt[5]{y}$ **8B)** $\sqrt{x} \cdot \sqrt[6]{x}$

8C) $\left(\sqrt[6]{b^3}\right)^4$ **8D)** $\left(\sqrt[5]{b^{10}}\right)^3$

Solutions:

8A) $y^{\frac{7}{10}}$ **8B)** $x^{\frac{2}{3}}$

8C) b^2 **8D)** b^6

Chapter 10: Quadratic Equations

Section 10.1
EXAMPLE 1:
Solve each equation.

1A) $x^2 - 100 = 0$

1B) $x^2 - 144 = 0$

Solutions:

1A) $x = \pm 10$ **1B)** $x = \pm 12$

EXAMPLE 2:
Solve each equation.

2A) $x^2 + 9 = 130$

2B) $x^2 + 25 = 50$

Solutions:

2A) $x = \pm 11$ **2B)** $x = \pm 5$

EXAMPLE 3:
Solve each equation.

3A) $x^2 - 13 = 0$

3B) $x^2 - 10 = 0$

Solutions:

3A) $x = \pm\sqrt{13}$

3B) $x = \pm\sqrt{10}$

EXAMPLE 4:
Solve each equation

4A) $(x - 5)^2 = 16$

4B) $(x - 2)^2 = 9$

Solutions:

4A) $x = 1$ or $x = 9$

4B) $x = -1$ or $x = 5$

EXAMPLE 5:
Solve each equation.

5A) $(4x + 1)^2 - 3 = 24$

5B) $(3x - 2)^2 + 4 = 16$

Solutions:

5A) $x = \dfrac{-1 \pm 3\sqrt{3}}{4}$

5B) $x = \dfrac{2 \pm 2\sqrt{3}}{3}$

EXAMPLE 6:
6A) A rectangle's width is 0.75 as long as it's length. If the area of the rectangle is 30 square cm, find the dimensions of the rectangle.

6B) The height of a triangle is 1.65 times as long as the base of the triangle. If the area of the triangle is 15 square feet, find the height and base of the triangle.

Solutions:

6A) The length is approximately 6.3 cm, so the width is approximately 4.7 cm

6B) The base is approximately 4.3 feet, so the height is approximately 7.0 feet

Section 10.2
EXAMPLE 1:
Solve each equation by completing the square.

1A) $x^2 + 8x - 20 = 0$

1B) $x^2 + 16x - 17 = 0$

Solutions:

1A) $x = -10, 2$

1B) $x = -17, 1$

EXAMPLE 2:
Solve each equation by completing the square.

2A) $x^2 - 6x - 16 = 0$

2B) $x^2 - 14x + 13 = 0$

Solutions:

2A) $x = -2, 8$ **2B)** $x = 1, 13$

EXAMPLE 3:
Solve each equation by completing the square.

3A) $x^2 = 7x + 8$

3B) $x^2 = x + 2$

Solutions:

3A) $x = -1, 8$ **3B)** $x = -1, 2$

EXAMPLE 4:
Solve each equation by completing the square.

4A) $x^2 - 18x + 9 = 0$

4B) $x^2 - 20x + 12 = 0$

Solutions:

4A) $x = 9 \pm 6\sqrt{2}$

4B) $x = 10 \pm 8\sqrt{22}$

EXAMPLE 5:
Solve each equation by completing the square.

5A) $4x^2 - 20x + 20 = 0$

5B) $6x^2 + 24x + 12 = 0$

Solutions:

5A) $x = \dfrac{3 \pm \sqrt{5}}{2}$

5B) $x = -2 \pm \sqrt{2}$

Section 10.3
EXAMPLE 1:
Use the quadratic equation to solve each equation.

1A) $x^2 - x + 12 = 0$

1B) $x^2 + 9x + 14 = 0$

Solutions:

1A) $x = -3$ or $x = 4$

1B) $x = -2$ or $x = -7$

EXAMPLE 2:
Use the quadratic formula to solve each equation.

2A) $6x^2 + x - 1 = 0$

2B) $20x^2 + 13x + 2 = 0$

Solutions:

2A) $x = -\dfrac{1}{2}, \dfrac{1}{3}$

2B) $x = -\dfrac{1}{4}, -\dfrac{2}{5}$

EXAMPLE 3:
Use the quadratic formula to solve each equation.

3A) $2x^2 + 7x - 3 = 0$

3B) $3x^2 - 2x - 11 = 0$

Solutions:

3A) $x = \dfrac{-7 \pm \sqrt{73}}{4}$

3B) $x = \dfrac{1 \pm \sqrt{34}}{3}$